PITCHERWITS®

VOLUME 3

Daily Mail

PITCHERWITS®

200 OF THE *DAILY MAIL'S* MOST POPULAR PICTURE PUZZLE

VOLUME **3**

hamlyn

An Hachette UK Company
www.hachette.co.uk

First published in Great Britain in 2017 by
Hamlyn, a division of Octopus Publishing Group Ltd
Carmelite House, 50 Victoria Embankment
London EC4Y 0DZ
www.octopusbooks.co.uk

ISBN 978-0-60063-491-1

A CIP catalogue record for this book is available from the British Library.

Printed and bound in the UK

10 9 8 7 6 5 4 3 2 1

Acknowledgements

Production Manager: Emily Arnold
Page make up: Press Association – Deborah Kelly
Sub-editors: Lisa Allen, Richard Colfer, Sophie Letheren,
Caroline Lomas, Lucy Whetman

PITCHERWITS®

Professor Rebus

Pitcherwits is the crossword where some of the clues are pictures. The mixture of cryptic and picture clues, combined with Professor Rebus's unique sense of humour, will keep you entertained for hours.

Top Tip from the Prof
Remember to say what you see and perhaps even try out a different accent!

About Professor Rebus

The Prof lives and works in his beloved Derbyshire. He is married with three children, three step-children and three grandchildren. He is interested in engineering, education and the English language – especially phonetics. He enjoys walks in the Derbyshire countryside with his wife, listening to and playing music. He likes horse-riding, rowing, fell-walking and rock climbing, and dreams of exploring the Lake District by microlight one day. He loves the thought of his puzzles making people smile up and down the country on a daily basis.

PUZZLE 1

ACROSS

1 Picture clue

5 Picture clue

8 Bury in between (5)

9 Paper benches? (5)

10 Garden nuisance - showing boredom (5)

12 Clumsily lower spur wheel (5)

14 Picture clue

15 Picture clue

13 Art we designed for Adam's ale (5)

DOWN

1 Picture clue

2 Coast damage at race place (5)

3 Sore and cruel twist (5)

4 Picture clue

6 Picture clue

7 Picture clue

11 Neuron? What a cheek! (5)

ACROSS

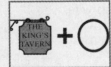

1a. Pervading (2,3,6)

5a. Timeless answer... (7)

14a. Device that clicks? (7)

15a. Now start counting... (3,3,5)

DOWN

1d. Questionable action! (7,4)

4d. Where you can't hear a pin drop (4,7)

6d. Planely, it's a take-out (7)

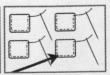

7d. So on, and followers (2,5)

PITCHERWITS 3

ACROSS

1 Picture clue
5 Snake with feathers? (3)
6 Edge of the perimeter (3)
7 Picture clue
10 Donkey's a bit biassed... (3)
11 Set fair, strangely, for mirror's verdict (7)
12 Via person in front (3)
13 Picture clue
16 In 60 mins, what can be said of us? (3)
17 Into getting insulation rating (3)
18 Picture clue

DOWN

1 Picture clue
2 Frolic, from personal deduction (4)
3 Care about part of the region (4)
4 Picture clue
5 Picture clue
8 Blood line has a rota error (5)
9 Picture clue
14 Dashingly cut below the knee (4)
15 Go on about the area you can't... (2-2)

ACROSS

1a. Instructions - for clothes? (4,5)

7a. Jesus story (7)

13a. Has actions in rows? (7)

18a. About to strike out (4,5)

DOWN

1d. Looks after (5,3)

4d. Bulbs out by now... (4,6)

5d. For one who's a bit cutting (10)

9d. Cameos, maybe (3,5)

PUZZLE 3

PITCHERWITS 3

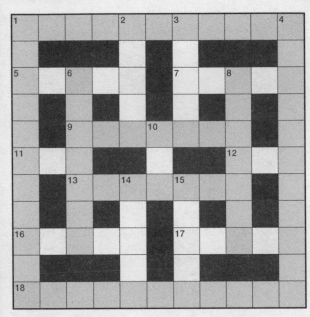

ACROSS

1 Picture clue
5 Agile - but cold? (5)
7 Reproaches (painlessly) for furniture style (5)
9 Picture clue
11 Throw off floating cereal (3)
12 Frogmarch out of circle line (3)
13 Picture clue
16 In vain, offer to score by deflection (2-3)
17 Lag in trouble in line-up (5)
18 Picture clue

DOWN

1 Picture clue
2 Verse about her plans to get my back up (5)
3 Food strained in unadulterated way (5)
4 Picture clue
6 Picture clue
8 Picture clue
10 ...and up to cell molecule (1,1,1)
14 How soldiers can dress, civilly (5)
15 Want rough force to have a nasal sound (5)

ACROSS

1a. Middling... (11)

9a. Such beautiful creatures (3,4)

13a. Confined types (7)

18a. This'll slow things up! (7,4)

DOWN

1d. ...with an iron grip? (11)

4d. Maverick type (5,6)

6d. Porch (or topic about it) (7)

8d. Where you fly off-piste? (7)

PITCHERWITS 3

ACROSS

1 Picture clue

7 Ransack with a gun (5)

8 Picture clue

11 Pace of the totem pole (5)

13 Any Londoner has it, materially (5)

14 Picture clue

16 Watering hole for flower arrangers? (5)

18 Picture clue

DOWN

2 Lout (of a sort) (3)

3 Picture clue

4 Resting on single T-shirt (4)

5 Picture clue

6 Picture clue

9 Picture clue

10 I do loathe a bit of a false god (4)

12 Unkind sort of average (4)

15 Slipped, so computer can't read it? (4)

17 Wicked bit of absinthe (3)

ACROSS

1a. "Don't panic!" types (4-6)

8a. Discouraging (7)

14a. Frankness (7)

18a. Throwaway answer! (10)

DOWN

3d. Quietly does it (3,5)

5d. Canine persistence? (10)

6d. It's drawn - out! (10)

9d. Principally it's a highway (4,4)

ACROSS

1 Picture clue
5 Picture clue
8 Last 'ouch' to bestow (5)
9 Arrangement is upset badly (3-2)
10 Tear I make up is cross (5)
12 Following a fret can be confusing (5)
14 Picture clue
15 Picture clue

DOWN

1 Picture clue
2 About the odd word - it's a mob (5)
3 Spy who's a bit of a nice guy? (5)
4 Picture clue
6 Picture clue
7 Picture clue
11 He can sell you a damn' mess! (5)
13 Tom, digitally finished (5)

ACROSS

1a. ...of soda? (11)

5a. Essential engine tubing (3,4)

14a. Marcel Mimer (7)

15a. Hot off the press - for 16th century! (6,5)

DOWN

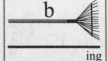

1d. This'll slow you down! (5,6)

4d. This is way out! (6,5)

6d. This'll slow you down too! (3,4)

7d. Flood condition (2,5)

PITCHERWITS 3

ACROSS

1 Picture clue
5 ...and goes back to coding, genetically (1,1,1)
6 Potter in line, so to speak? (3)
7 Picture clue
10 As soon as it's cut, donkey shows (3)
11 Cord put into artefact (7)
12 Profit that's greasy? (3)
13 Picture clue
16 Roman eggs all done? (3)
17 Bit of compensation for the writer (3)
18 Picture clue

DOWN

1 Picture clue
2 Always a high achiever in the end (4)
3 Hear the pull of the entrance (4)
4 Picture clue
5 Picture clue
8 An odd sort of afterthought (3-2)
9 Picture clue
14 Fruity sort of New Zealander? (4)
15 Aim of the game! (4)

ACROSS

1a. Far South, in ancient Israel (9)

7a. Motor on track? (7)

13a. "Order!" (7)

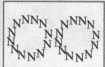
18a. Goes round... (9)

DOWN

1d. ...to make the ball bounce up (8)

4d. It draws you, but not in ink (10)

5d. Reckon to be bad (10)

9d. Where Moggy panics? (8)

ACROSS

1 Picture clue

5 Picture clue

7 Junction at hill and... 'Wallop'! (5)

8 Sixth kind of logic (5)

9 Safeguard, without ages taken to hoax (5)

11 Exactly how the fruit gets a bad start? (5)

12 Picture clue

13 Picture clue

DOWN

1 Picture clue

2 Sick of being nourished - vertically? (3,2)

3 Wants to send round kind of mail (5)

4 Picture clue

5 Picture clue

6 Picture clue

10 Wilt should end with poor uptake (5)

11 Choice sort of number? (5)

ACROSS

1a. 'Twitcher' (4,7)

5a. Compensation (7)

12a. Screen supports of old (1,6)

13a. Top gears? (4,3,4)

DOWN

1d. March like a wally! (2,3,2,4)

4d. Veg that can sprint? (6,5)

5d. Custard partner (7)

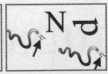

6d. They're spoofs! (4-3)

PITCHERWITS 3

ACROSS

1 Picture clue
5 Picture clue
9 Spoil what gin did to mothers (4)
10 Rummage around inside for kit (4)
11 Runner who is a racehorse (5)
12 Thermal ratings of familiar clothing (4)
14 Annexe - to go with a prayer? (4)
15 Picture clue
18 Picture clue

DOWN

1 Picture clue
2 Picture clue
3 'Tis about to be briefly, so it is! (3)
4 Relatively speaking, it's our brightest star (3)
6 By gum! Follow rigidly? (5,2)
7 Primate spotted in Chesapeake (3)
8 Picture clue
10 Picture clue
13 Fuel the chatter (3)
16 Pal in trouble? It's a bit of a mountain (3)
17 It's plant juice, fool! (3)

ACROSS

1a. Leaders - on paper? (10)

5a. Putin types (8)

15a. Finishes with the knitting... (5,3)

18a. Qualities of landlords? (10)

DOWN

1d. Dynamic (9)

2d. Occurrences of trousers? (4-3)

8d. Are they odder? (9)

10d. Lose fitness (not weight!) (4,3)

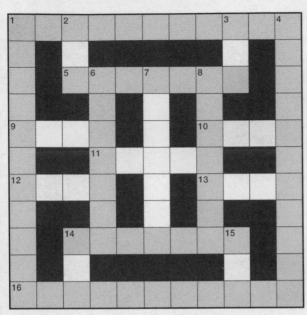

ACROSS

1 Picture clue
5 Picture clue
9 Writer, made of wash-tub iron (4)
10 Called, having managed the force (4)
11 Model of amino structure (5)
12 Opposed to, in the meantime... (4)
13 Frugal amounts to include festivity (4)
14 Picture clue
16 Picture clue

DOWN

1 Picture clue
2 Negative - sounds ropey... (3)
3 Simply not devious, little gremlin (3)
4 Picture clue

6 Picture clue
7 Romps, after eucalyptuses start to look like politicians (4-3)
8 Picture clue

14 Part of an isosceles triangle - Help! (1,1,1)
15 Myself, I'm a bit woebegone! (3)

ACROSS

1a. Garden shaping (11)

5a. Started to do (5,2)

14a. With feeling... (7)

16a. Scatterings (11)

DOWN

1d. That's logical... (4-7)

4d. Dutch way to settle bill? (5,6)

6d. Wrestle, mentally (7)

8d. It's vertical - honest! (7)

PITCHERWITS 3

ACROSS

1 Picture clue
6 Pig - with a reputation for being dull? (4)
7 Nothing - could lead by mouth, doctor (3)
8 Foundation said to sing low? (4)
9 Picture clue
11 Picture clue
14 Toni is sort of enthusiastic (4)
15 Crystal, in basic English... (3)
16 Split in the snowdrifts (4)
17 Picture clue

DOWN

1 Picture clue
2 Picture clue
3 A rota altered in the blood line (5)
4 Boredom of reunion - or not, maybe? (5)
5 Picture clue
10 Picture clue
12 She's as slippery as an eel (5)
13 Morse code for customs (5)

ACROSS

1a. Heard it's red, regularly! (5,5)

9a. They're moonstruck (8)

11a. Naughty, but nice! (5,3)

17a. Start some mayhem (5,1,4)

DOWN

1d. Not for the skinny! (6,4)

2d. Flower (not river) (7)

5d. Site for bangers? (10)

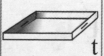

10d. Judas (7)

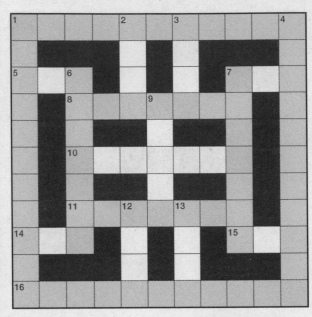

ACROSS

1 Picture clue

5 Bit juvenile on court? That's nothing! (3)

7 Swinish sort of iron? (3)

8 Picture clue

10 Hanger-on - in the plant world! (7)

11 Picture clue

14 Thing's about to sit (3)

15 Restored finally, in colour (3)

16 Picture clue

DOWN

1 Picture clue

2 Powder - the least alcoholic part (4)

3 Buffaloes - a bit succulent (4)

4 Picture clue

6 Picture clue

7 Picture clue

9 Bestow - finally to you, say? (5)

12 Crazy - for spanners? (4)

13 Pull down northern urban area (4)

ACROSS

1a. Held back (11)

8a. Goes over (7)

11a. Roof light (7)

16a. Is this obscene wealth? (5,6)

DOWN

1d. Giving forms - verbally (11)

4d. Cursive stroke? (5,6)

6d. Seeds for stews? (7)

7d. Book for musical prayers? (7)

PITCHERWITS 3

ACROSS

1 Picture clue

5 Picture clue

9 Three to break up riot (4)

10 She's found with oars replaced (4)

11 Dish of cooked tripe (5)

12 Does sets of scenes (4)

14 Swig of Mogul potion (4)

15 Picture clue

18 Picture clue

DOWN

1 Picture clue
2 Picture clue
3 Dutch one? That's for weeds! (3)
4 In court, will she go for you? (3)
6 Set up trap ten for blueprint (7)
7 Hot work from a duo (3)
8 Picture clue
10 Picture clue
13 Model-sounding drink (3)
16 Age of geranium cutting (3)
17 She's a bit believable! (3)

ACROSS

1a. Bricks across... (10)

5a. Over...and over? (8)

15a. They're going nowhere! (4,4)

18a. Get back up (10)

DOWN

1d. Direction (9)

2d. Chosen for Brussels (4-3)

8d. Mountain for Incey Wincey? (9)

10d. ...poorly maybe (5,2)

PITCHERWITS 3

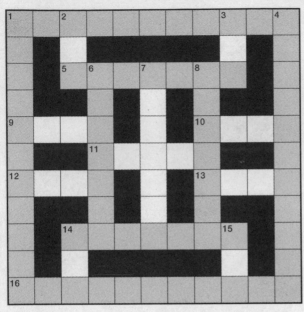

ACROSS

1 Picture clue

5 Picture clue

9 Lazy tickover? (4)

10 Last word in God talk! (4)

11 Protest that's bottomed? (3-2)

12 Aged form of aged surprise (4!)

13 Should end without power to remove (4)

14 Picture clue

16 Picture clue

DOWN

1 Picture clue

2 Lower type of fuel uptake (3)

3 Molecule in position (3)

4 Picture clue

6 Picture clue

7 Trod its way round change (7)

8 Picture clue

14 Smooth bit of talking, you cow! (3)

15 Google - mess at first! (3)

ACROSS

1a. Being nice to girl? Wrong! (11)

5a. Bank with sacks (allegedly) (7)

14a. Coming together (7)

16a. "Carry on," as flyers (6,5)

DOWN

1d. Launder - look, no hands! (7,4)

4d. They accommodate maturity (6,5)

6d. It's what you owe (4,3)

8d. Could be reckless... (7)

ACROSS

1 Picture clue

7 Rib to break, in flight path (5)

8 Do owe, somehow, that's courted (5)

9 Picture clue

11 Picture clue

14 Spooky sound of a nest (5)

15 Form of art we see in liquid (5)

16 Picture clue

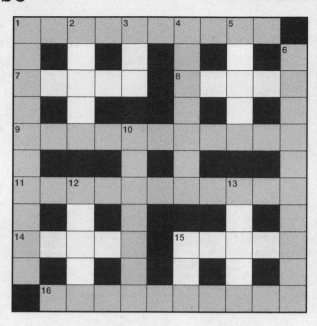

DOWN

1 Picture clue
2 Bleat about some furniture (5)
3 Rent permit (3)
4 Picture clue
5 Sub, about to turn (1-4)
6 Picture clue
10 Picture clue
12 Polo is a macro type (5)
13 It's everything musical (5)
15 Stack of notes wasted when set out (3)

ACROSS

1a. Chickened? (7,3)

9a. "Meet anon..." (3,3,5)

11a. Stopping control (5,6)

16a. Staple (but not to paper!) (6,4)

DOWN

1d. Reading person (10)

4d. 'Spare' dog nail (3-4)

6d. Talented one - surprise! (1,4,5)

10d. Porridge to a male? It's crazy! (7)

ACROSS

1 Picture clue
5 Picture clue
8 Religious leader I swam into trouble with (5)
9 Acrylic fibre, said to be at full stretch (5)
10 Not possible - scrap the scales? (2,3)
12 /DO, said to be a visual accompaniment (5)
14 Picture clue
15 Picture clue

DOWN

1 Picture clue
2 Letter at first is Greek to me (5)
3 Bits of peel round the Times? Throw it out! (5)
4 Picture clue
6 Picture clue
7 Picture clue
11 Squeeze wiring I discarded (5)
13 Frightful locks? (5)

ACROSS

1a. Concisely... (2,1,8)

5a. Said - with a tube? (5,2)

14a. Set apart (7)

15a. Licit, but sore? (5,6)

DOWN

1d. Just not necessary (11)

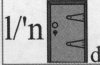

4d. Mr and Mrs Nawda's daughter, Laura? (3,3,5)

6d. Let in on (apologies!) (5,2)

7d. It's a picture - how moving! (7)

PITCHERWITS 3

ACROSS

1 Picture clue
5 Feather one stored in airing-cupboard (3)
6 Polyethylene has it, however... (3)
7 Picture clue
10 Eggs sound like they're done (3)
11 Chicken is so retro, somehow (7)
12 Cry like a slob outside (3)
13 Picture clue
16 An age of literature... (3)
17 Thing's found in gritstone (3)
18 Picture clue

DOWN

1 Picture clue
2 Keen on a bit of badminton (4)
3 Copy the sound of a screech owl (4)
4 Picture clue
5 Picture clue
8 Seen as a large part of the nose (5)
9 Picture clue
14 Toff from Argentina (4)
15 Try earning a bit - for a long time (4)

ACROSS

1a. Rumoured... (9)

7a. They're not common! (3,4)

13a. Mainly (7)

18a. After all that... it wasn't gold! (9)

DOWN

1d. Wary fear of becoming traveller... (8)

4d. Takes apart (10)

5d. Soon... (6,4)

9d. Early medical procedures (5,3)

PITCHERWITS 3

ACROSS

1 Picture clue
5 Standoff always produces cheap meat (5)
7 Boat repair comes to nothing with ban (5)
9 Picture clue
11 Wonder claimed for a mineral (3)
12 Coat masked in diplomacy (3)
13 Picture clue
16 Make sense - totally? (3,2)
17 Led on to become ancient (5)
18 Picture clue

DOWN

1 Picture clue
2 She reformed Alice (5)
3 Express - totally! (5)
4 Picture clue
6 Picture clue
8 Picture clue
10 Accommodating place in Cincinnati (3)
14 Speedy way to knock identity, briefly (5)
15 Anguish of confidante aunt (5)

ACROSS

1a. It's municipal! (4,7)

9a. Ran the meeting in her acid style (7)

13a. Fighter plane's a twister (7)

18a. A des res that's secondary? (7,4)

DOWN

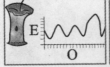

1d. Work out those steps! (11)

4d. Makes holes in your pockets... (5,6)

6d. Like a diamond (not in the sky) (7)

8d. Grumpy's in one (3,4)

PITCHERWITS 3

ACROSS

1 Picture clue
7 Get rid, in strange way, of Madagascan lemur (5)
8 Picture clue
11 Levitate at small hospital surplus (5)
13 Altogether now - play! (5)
14 Picture clue
16 Winston's gesture, saving a lost plan (1-4)
18 Picture clue

DOWN

2 Relieve from pride (3)
3 Picture clue
4 Beige cure, roughly (4)
5 Picture clue
6 Picture clue
9 Picture clue
10 Dextrous, but fed up over square (4)
12 Bloodline said to be conceited (4)
15 Smooth sort of club? (4)
17 Sprinkled a bit of marking fluid... (3)

ACROSS

1a. All soppy? (6-4)

8a. Self-deceived (7)

14a. Met (not office) (3,4)

18a. Vertical caress? (10)

DOWN

3d. Tart downfall is corrosive! (4,4)

5d. Weedy? They're not really! (10)

6d. With a massive personal pump? (3-7)

9d. What's remaining is a daft fret, love (4-4)

PITCHERWITS 3

ACROSS

1 Picture clue
5 Picture clue
8 Slow to score as collar got trimmed (5)
9 Frequently seen in softeners (5)
10 What the cook would give to be awake! (5)
12 Overheard when dropped just under the roof (5)
14 Picture clue
15 Picture clue

DOWN

1 Picture clue
2 Me sir? In some ways I'm Scrooge! (5)
3 Interchange that's lifeless (5)
4 Picture clue
6 Picture clue
7 Picture clue
11 Understood it's an attic conversion (5)
13 Dvorak right out of it - disorientating booze! (5)

ACROSS

1a. Boundary-making (11)

5a. Strange respect for the ghost (7)

14a. Jumped about (7)

15a. Cinders, you shall... (2,2,3,4)

DOWN

1d. Taking from internet (11)

4d. Public opinion movement (11)

6d. Holiday for the selfish? (3,4)

7d. Not enough distance... (3,4)

PITCHERWITS 3

ACROSS

1 Picture clue
5 Motor to come across in Monte Carlo (3)
6 Realm with no artist leaves only a tree... (3)
7 Picture clue
10 Junction often said to be in cup (3)
11 From Lou, somehow, enough to fill a space (7)
12 Pleasing bit of meadow (3)
13 Picture clue
16 Solution's not in... (3)
17 Not even strange (3)
18 Picture clue

DOWN

1 Picture clue
2 Mean kind of label (4)
3 Make it again - out of boredom! (2-2)
4 Picture clue
5 Picture clue
8 Road from the manor (5)
9 Picture clue
14 Detour with trip at end (4)
15 Obliged to be led out round the desert (4)

ACROSS

1a. Go bust - yesterday! (4,5)

7a. Descartes thinks he is... (4,3)

13a. Harsh sounding (7)

18a. It's reasonable... (4,5)

DOWN

1d. Shading hard to pin down (4,4)

4d. Got rid of (10)

5d. Taking away (7,3)

9d. Lonely, long-distance runner writer (8)

ACROSS

1 Picture clue
5 Picture clue
7 Taxi, all stripped down and rotational (5)
8 Should have lost his marbles, according to Greeks! (5)
9 A fret about later... (5)
11 Such inoffensive bits of cotton twill (5)
12 Picture clue
13 Picture clue

DOWN

1 Picture clue
2 Fine welcome - bit handy on flight (5)
3 Lineage, not an allegiance mediaevally (5)
4 Picture clue
5 Picture clue
6 Picture clue
10 Learn about kidney stuff (5)
11 Teacher, trying to include a bit of silica (5)

ACROSS

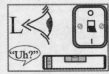

1a. Be at same elevation (3,2,1,5)

5a. They keep woodcutters in trim (3,4)

12a. Tinny place to work! (7)

13a. Cogitation - twice (11)

DOWN

1d. Expected - for ages! (4-7)

4d. ...before you can run? (5,2,4)

5d. What a nerve (7)

6d. It's to imply... (7)

PITCHERWITS 3

ACROSS

1 Picture clue
5 Picture clue
9 Era to give out from the right (4)
10 Dumb location to site an axis (4)
11 Steer around flavouring compound (5)
12 Wandered, only to wade out like an anorak (4)
14 More than finished! (4)
15 Picture clue
18 Picture clue

DOWN

1 Picture clue
2 Picture clue
3 Said to be a line of fish eggs (3)
4 Deceive the young one (3)
6 Open up a tin rim of gin and vermouth (7)
7 Finally, everyone's inside (3)
8 Picture clue
10 Picture clue
13 Sore element of strawberries (3)
16 Ancient type of testament (3)
17 Succeed in twinkling a little (3)

ACROSS

1a. Post-ring syndrome (5,5)

5a. Might taste nicer... (4-4)

15a. Blowing towards the ground? (8)

18a. Destitute (4,3,3)

DOWN

1d. Modelled (9)

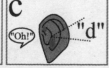
2d. Stuck - are you? (7)

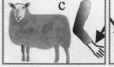
8d. Said to be wholly a meal (9)

10d. Thought moodily of chicks with the editor! (7)

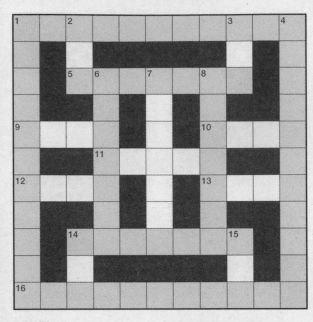

ACROSS

1 Picture clue
5 Picture clue
9 Concept - to ride about in? (4)
10 Vocabulary of jungle king (4)
11 Speedy place for white-knuckle rafting? (5)
12 Feeling awkward a bit - hence the gape (4)
13 Opposing form of praying mantis (4)
14 Picture clue
16 Picture clue

DOWN

1 Picture clue
2 Shouted without the hut not being in (3)
3 Bitter herb - the French way (3)
4 Picture clue
6 Picture clue
7 Colder, in piper composition (7)
8 Picture clue
14 Fairy made in Delft (3)
15 Perceive, say, the ocean (3)

ACROSS

1a. With no hassle (7-4)

5a. Not for skating on (4,3)

14a. They're in! (7)

16a. At maximum flow (2,4,5)

DOWN

1d. Film - from long ago (3,4,3,1)

4d. Talking of daleks... (11)

6d. Now listen up! (7)

8d. Hearty? (7)

PITCHERWITS 3

ACROSS

1 Picture clue
6 Ale said to become one (4)
7 Shirt said to be for a meal (3)
8 Bed I made to stay in (4)
9 Picture clue
11 Picture clue
14 ...as well as in the final song (4)
15 Ore turns out to be fish eggs! (3)
16 Where coal is said to appear? (4)
17 Picture clue

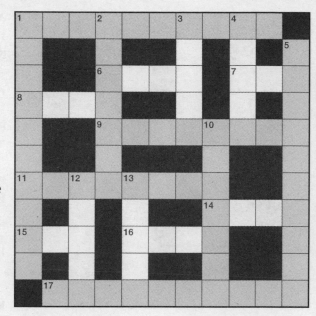

DOWN

1 Picture clue
2 Picture clue
3 Quiet mat shows indifference (5)
4 Duo to try and exceed (5)
5 Picture clue
10 Picture clue
12 A rope, all tangled in musical item (5)
13 Place with a salty racecourse? (5)

ACROSS

1a. Opposite of Jane Austen novel? (10) 9a. Ends call (5,3) 11a. In the right way (8) 17a. They are attractive! (3,7)

DOWN

  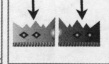 

1d. ...so block in (6-4) 2d. Get un-drunk? (5,2) 5d. 'Two and sixes' in days of yore (4,6) 10d. End Almighty call! (3,4)

PITCHERWITS 3

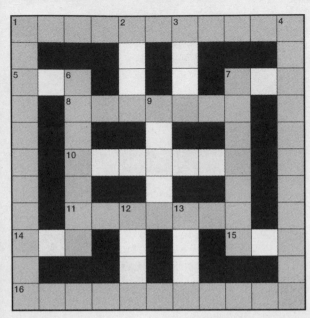

ACROSS

1 Picture clue
5 Limit of top gear (3)
7 Set up for oil in N Sea, say (3)
8 Picture clue
10 Counsellor to drive as if mad (7)
11 Picture clue
14 States in accusations that... (3)
15 Prophet of shapeliness - he's central (3)
16 Picture clue

DOWN

1 Picture clue
2 Leader is of them, I realise (4)
3 Drawback the city district (4)
4 Picture clue
6 Picture clue
7 Picture clue
9 'Midi-omelette', in a manner of speaking (5)
12 Title? It's a real mess (4)
13 Example of a test... (4)

ACROSS

1a. Round at the front of the 'van (6,5)

8a. It's to shorten (7)

11a. Single substance - in a kettle? (7)

16a. Claims some results... (11)

DOWN

1d. Packman - can lift the irons, say? (4,2,5)

4d. Do they involve illumination? (5,6)

6d. Cure-all (7)

7d. Put pen to paper - again (2-5)

PITCHERWITS 3

ACROSS

1 Picture clue
5 Picture clue
9 Flick over strong cheek (4)
10 Norwegian boss featuring in school average (4)
11 Heathen has little silver in the pot (5)
12 Libel, set to have alternative (4)
14 Male deer in hospital pictures (4)
15 Picture clue
18 Picture clue

DOWN

1 Picture clue
2 Picture clue
3 "Eggs are done!" (3)
4 Woman who's out of blusher (3)
6 Talking of being weary... (5-2)
7 She's short, and a bit under-valued (3)
8 Picture clue
10 Picture clue
13 Chop suey's for her! (3)
16 Visual agreement put on up (3)
17 Jump on one in beer-making (3)

ACROSS

1a. They go just above ankles (5,5)

5a. Split the bill (2,6)

15a. Desk (well, sort of...) (8)

18a. ...not on the floor, surely? (4,6)

DOWN

1d. Meat for a bullish bet? (9)

2d. Chanter, from Scotland (7)

8d. Decade (so last century!) (9)

10d. Current, gone hot, cooked (2,3,2)

PITCHERWITS 3

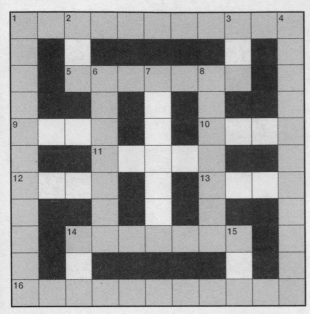

ACROSS

1 Picture clue

5 Picture clue

9 Cook ratatouille - with a bit of veg. (4)

10 Killer whale for canning centrally (4)

11 Bit of coral reef is somehow 'loppy' (5)

12 Boundary, made of hedgerows (4)

13 Ornate seat from the Orient (4)

14 Picture clue

16 Picture clue

DOWN

1 Picture clue

2 ...because it's a little lettuce (3)

3 Sloppy soil - a bit muddled? (3)

4 Picture clue

6 Picture clue

7 Owl's law - drawn up for the bird (7)

8 Picture clue

14 Container - doesn't sound right (3)

15 Adherents of that woman (3)

ACROSS

1a. Like a table-cloth, maybe (4-7)

5a. Salted away (7)

14a. For a clean flight? (3-4)

16a. What the frog was made to do? (6,5)

DOWN

1d. Impossibly careless thing to do? (4,7)

4d. You might, you knitwit! (4,1,6)

6d. Flying one for daring young men (7)

8d. They're running away, people! (7)

PITCHERWITS 3

ACROSS

1 Picture clue

7 Ponder over the litter (5)

8 Tin (or compound) is a short beginning (5)

9 Picture clue

11 Picture clue

14 Add. (That's your lot!) (5)

15 Police warning - she's a temptress! (5)

16 Picture clue

DOWN

1 Picture clue

2 Float about on high... (5)

3 Put on up, as a gesture (3)

4 Picture clue

5 It's about a terse chemical compound (5)

6 Picture clue

10 Picture clue

12 Bury inert plans (5)

13 Push rubbish in bush (5)

15 Spot the bishop's place (3)

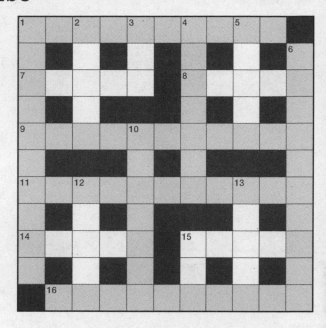

ACROSS

1a. IQ - or is that "high Q"? (10)

9a. Releasing hold (7,4)

11a. Something horrid for the gossips... (5,6)

16a. Can be got across (10)

DOWN

1d. How printers used to be! (6-4)

4d. Because of money that should be paid? (5,2)

6d. 'Plumptiousness'! (10)

10d. Creepy! (3-4)

PITCHERWITS 3

ACROSS

1 Picture clue
5 Picture clue
8 Relieves beasties - at a bit of a loss? (5)
9 Dance carved out from amboyna (5)
10 She's an aid in trouble all right! (5)
12 Tones that jar at the start (5)
14 Picture clue
15 Picture clue

DOWN

1 Picture clue
2 Vertical jumps in the home counties? (5)
3 Hello Cumbria! Dr Temp. there? (5)
4 Picture clue
6 Picture clue
7 Picture clue
11 Small department with hospital has profundity (5)
13 Promise to use bad language? (5)

ACROSS

1a. Celebratory one round the ear? (7,4)

5a. Wit, maybe? (7)

14a. Get ready for this... (7)

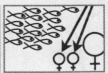

15a. Little lady learners (11)

DOWN

1d. Irresistible lorries? (11)

4d. For sections of ratios? (11)

6d. Set-up at odds in Northern parts, USA (7)

7d. Raffle, at bloom's demise (7)

PITCHERWITS 3

ACROSS

1 Picture clue
5 Snake nesting (in Gazebo, actually) (3)
6 One or two, say, in total (3)
7 Picture clue
10 Use some skittles for equipment (3)
11 Sufferer, with no more legal force (7)
12 Molecule is in position.... (3)
13 Picture clue
16 Rug said to be rather dull (3)
17 Warning ring goes off when pale (3)
18 Picture clue

DOWN

1 Picture clue
2 Reminder seen in extreme moment (4)
3 Footwear to drive away, say (4)
4 Picture clue
5 Picture clue
8 Mad sort of pastry (5)
9 Picture clue
14 Close to Northern listener (4)
15 Give out - and about time too! (4)

ACROSS

1a. Panned the roasting meat? (9)

7a. End of the bargain? (5,2)

13a. Like an eagle's? (4,3)

18a. How little cog relates to big? (4,5)

DOWN

1d. Previously... (4,4)

4d. Seeing briefly (8,2)

5d. Literary activity? Not! (10)

9d. Station - without a platform (5,3)

ACROSS

1 Picture clue
5 Dish of tripe? Ugh! (5)
7 Those pianists - a bit like old photos (5)
9 Picture clue
11 Solid or not, it's beginning to be relative (3)
12 Vehicle is scary without South Yorkshire element (3)
13 Picture clue
16 Manipulative sort of employers? (5)
17 Scam (ongoing) is part surrounded by... (5)
18 Picture clue

DOWN

1 Picture clue
2 Lift is hot, sort of (5)
3 A big lump, backing the tea (5)
4 Picture clue
6 Picture clue
8 Picture clue
10 Renovation uncovers eggs (3)
14 Seed case? That's a bit contestable (5)
15 Tell off the Sunday dinner (5)

ACROSS

1a. Metallically callous? (4-7)

9a. River to Chesapeake (7)

13a. Little Big Lake (7)

18a. Mainly, they are the bosses (3,8)

DOWN

1d. Check out these? (7,4)

4d. Said to be re-mote? (11)

6d. One to stave off? (3,4)

8d. Windy, but small (7)

PITCHERWITS 3

ACROSS

1 Picture clue
7 Risen from water wash (5)
8 Picture clue
11 Tiny weights should end with woolly males (5)
13 Headgear Tara takes one in for (5)
14 Picture clue
16 Make foolish, when saddled in the middle (5)
18 Picture clue

DOWN

2 Have some of the Crown Jewels (3)
3 Picture clue
4 Melt saw - with a lisp! (4)
5 Picture clue
6 Picture clue
9 Picture clue
10 2-D space - a real start (4)
12 Single 10 - exists as a centre (4)
15 Pins up the bargain (4)
17 Gamepiece of expediency (3)

ACROSS

1a. Soothing (10)

8a. Skinny sort of dwellings (7)

14a. Loser is amazed to be a burger (7)

18a. What a sucker! (7,3)

DOWN

3d. Got in a flap alone? (4,4)

5d. Now that's smoother! (10)

6d. Hot dog environment (6,4)

9d. "Easy does it..." (2,6)

ACROSS

1 Picture clue

5 Picture clue

8 No scissors for director's version (5)

9 Freakily - far out (and about) for Aussie warbler (5)

10 The cheek of the pie? (5)

12 They're dummies - in code (5)

14 Picture clue

15 Picture clue

DOWN

1 Picture clue

2 Atomic sort of Greek architecture? (5)

3 Airless imperial drive (5)

4 Picture clue

6 Picture clue

7 Picture clue

11 Top secret in WW2, but now in catapult range (5)

13 Composer - was he a to-do one? (5)

ACROSS

1a. Avian informer (1,6,4)

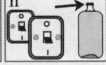

5a. No French arrest is 24/7... (3-4)

14a. News of ocean movements? (7)

15a. Weakens - seriously? (11)

DOWN

1d. Prickly medicine! (11)

4d. Do they give you cards? (11)

6d. Score settled? (7)

7d. Accepted (5,2)

PITCHERWITS 3

ACROSS

1 Picture clue
5 ...and back to genetic coding (1,1,1)
6 Total number of possums (3)
7 Picture clue
10 Short thanks you'll get for bitumen (3)
11 Almost taking the boat out (5,2)
12 Not back to heavyweight (3)
13 Picture clue
16 Please find bit of grazing enclosed... (3)
17 Youth from Bangladesh (3)
18 Picture clue

DOWN

1 Picture clue
2 Member of climbing club (4)
3 Rubbish! It's a bovine load (4)
4 Picture clue
5 Picture clue
8 Fob off fabulous designs as common (5)
9 Picture clue
14 A new version to bring to solid food (4)
15 Bit of leaf-curl, sucker! (4)

ACROSS

1a. Tinny sort of food? (5,4)

7a. Four by four fronting (4-3)

13a. Foster mother for Romulus and Remus (3-4)

18a. Rate lower (9)

DOWN

1d. Of interest to money people? (4,4)

4d. It's just a just attitude (4-6)

5d. Repro. furniture that's upset? (10)

9d. Where to buy bargains? (4,4)

PITCHERWITS 3

ACROSS

1 Picture clue

5 Picture clue

7 One more time, it's a plus (5)

8 Popeye's pal, useful for oil (5)

9 Sun is held back in nasal cavity (5)

11 Colossal sort - runs rings round Saturn (5)

12 Picture clue

13 Picture clue

DOWN

1 Picture clue

2 Gem, as only revealed by a craftsman (5)

3 Edit tons of the same (5)

4 Picture clue

5 Picture clue

6 Picture clue

10 Skilled worker sees mist swirling over hospital (5)

11 Tangled roots above the hips (5)

ACROSS

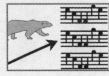

1a. Naval display, say? (4,7)

5a. Or a computer display? (7)

12a. Before being posh... (5,2)

13a. She's a noble sort (11)

DOWN

1d. Answer's bang on! (3,4,4)

4d. They're digital (11)

5d. Plans, maybe? (5,2)

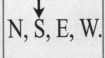

6d. Suggest (5,2)

PITCHERWITS 3

ACROSS

1 Picture clue

5 Picture clue

9 Dispatch disc from walkway (4)

10 Aaron's problem golden baby (4)

11 All on becoming - that's plain (5)

12 Service that's blue? (4)

14 Over, and about to wander (4)

15 Picture clue

18 Picture clue

DOWN

1 Picture clue
2 Picture clue
3 Impatient start - for a gremlin! (3)
4 Acquired a bit of anger (3)
6 Attack talk of condiment on its own (7)
7 Released from the meadow (3)
8 Picture clue
10 Picture clue
13 Vowels have promise (initially) (3)
16 Purpose is a bit obtuse (3)
17 (In basic English) a crystal (3)

ACROSS

1a. Moses had 2 tablets here (5,5)

5a. Wrestles (8)

15a. Persian Gulfers (8)

18a. Hears (when shouldn't!) (10)

DOWN

1d. He was a constant physicist (3,6)

2d. Darkness frequency (7)

8d. ...so they won't collapse, then? (4,5)

10d. This one's less fine... (7)

PITCHERWITS 3

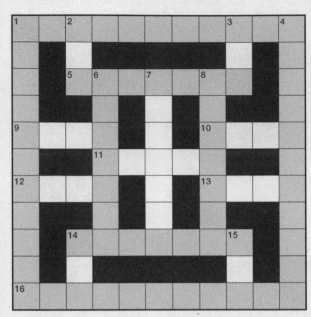

ACROSS

1 Picture clue
5 Picture clue
9 Whiskers with a hospital atmosphere (4)
10 Pile Uriah ended up with (4)
11 Potables set out roughly for Picasso (5)
12 Identical seam that's split open (4)
13 Lino cut to suit jungle king (4)
14 Picture clue
16 Picture clue

DOWN

1 Picture clue
2 Make a meal out of Chateaubriand (3)
3 Adventuresome part of Yorkshire flower (3)
4 Picture clue
6 Picture clue
7 Could a match be the Scottish play? (7)
8 Picture clue
14 Nothing from Manila... (3)
15 Steel key used to find moose (3)

ACROSS

1a. Scored zero (3,3,1,4)

5a. Make spray (7)

14a. Not any place at all... (7)

16a. ...plan B perhaps? (5,4,2)

DOWN

1d. Ready to buy (3,3,5)

4d. Antarctic bird - like a boss waiter? (4,7)

6d. Boat-sinker (7)

8d. Bachelors! - be not upset by this learner (7)

PITCHERWITS 3

ACROSS

1 Picture clue
6 It's on coupon at last (4)
7 Adoration can start as bother (3)
8 Much effort to cut down on cook (4)
9 Picture clue
11 Picture clue
14 Niffy half of table tennis? (4)
15 Colour seen in Derbyshire dales (3)
16 Laura's got an atmosphere (4)
17 Picture clue

DOWN

1 Picture clue
2 Picture clue
3 Ban all parts that are hackneyed! (5)
4 Inertia rarely produces headgear... (5)
5 Picture clue
10 Picture clue
12 Crazy do-gooder lost dog at cowboy show (5)
13 Am all taken aback at little camel (5)

ACROSS

1a. Give out, but not fail (10)

9a. Tum's a personal one! (4,4)

11a. Front runners? (8)

17a. Enjoy a meal in Paris (3,7)

DOWN

1d. Painful answer? (10)

2d. Deee-licious!! (7)

5d. This'll cost you! (7,3)

10d. Over... (2,5)

ACROSS

1 Picture clue
5 For sloppy feeders, it works anyway (3)
7 Cleaner part of the grazing (3)
8 Picture clue
10 Stick the vertical mire? (3,4)
11 Picture clue
14 Your old, but healthy at last (3)
15 It's an age of base rates.... (3)
16 Picture clue

DOWN

1 Picture clue
2 Turn out a car in the States (4)
3 Went about as a salamander (4)
4 Picture clue
6 Picture clue
7 Picture clue
9 Sound erased, but hiding below (5)
12 Throw the actors (4)
13 Fruit presumably not grown for its looks (4)

ACROSS

1a. Blind bit of track (7,4)

8a. Almost... (5,2)

11a. Soldier? - that's new! (7)

16a. Top trio, would you believe! (4,7)

DOWN

1d. Is it well needled? (5,6)

4d. Possibly a drama queen? (7,4)

6d. Cross sort of Oxford place? (7)

7d. For a bass player? (3,4)

PITCHERWITS 3

ACROSS

1 Picture clue

5 Picture clue

9 Informed by bell being rung allegedly (4)

10 Spirit made from only sound (4)

11 Crouching, yet hung out for the bloomers (5)

12 Estimate value of speed (4)

14 Generous type (4)

15 Picture clue

18 Picture clue

DOWN

1 Picture clue

2 Picture clue

3 Sayer - also a singer (3)

4 Stern bit of water travel (3)

6 Get better in a sofa refurbishing way? (7)

7 Also, Lotto ought to be reduced (3)

8 Picture clue

10 Picture clue

13 Dance type at the sink? (3)

16 Impressive start to the little devil! (3)

17 Peculiar bits of fodder (3)

ACROSS

1a. On his way soon! (5,5)

5a. Poetic - initially (8)

15a. Moses' missus (8)

18a. It'll be the making of this one (10)

DOWN

1d. ...on Monterey Bay, California (5,4)

2d. Badmouth (7)

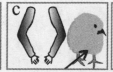

8d. Tranquilises? (5,4)

10d. Posh top gear! (4,3)

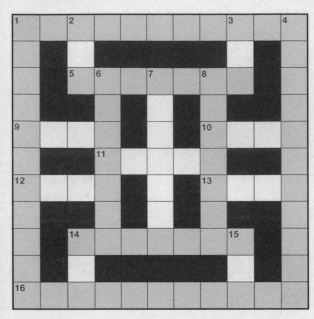

ACROSS

1 Picture clue
5 Picture clue
9 Terror of a ref. gone haywire (4)
10 Staunch kind of stalk (4)
11 Gave out in turn as being woolly (5)
12 Doer about to act again (4)
13 Horn, but back to a base (4)
14 Picture clue
16 Picture clue

DOWN

1 Picture clue
2 Bill's mate hiding in aircooler (3)
3 Get a mighty bit of hat (3)
4 Picture clue
6 Picture clue
7 Diver often croaking? (7)
8 Picture clue
14 Draw the neckwear (3)
15 Neat work setting for duo (3)

ACROSS

1a. It's just got faster! (11)

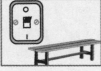

5a. Not up to usual standard (3,4)

14a. Bauble (7)

16a. Aims for the top (4,3,4)

DOWN

1d. Making tart (4-7)

4d. Got off - not on the wrong foot (11)

6d. Ardour (it's not 'arder')! (7)

8d. Badge to steer right round (7)

PITCHERWITS 3

ACROSS

1 Picture clue

7 "Amens" spelt out for minister's place (5)

8 Chimney-pot - not empty of cotton twill (5)

9 Picture clue

11 Picture clue

14 Roughly rouse, so as to be tender (5)

15 Fairy-like model finally gives out (5)

16 Picture clue

DOWN

1 Picture clue
2 Garden nuisance - can produce boredom (5)
3 Eventually she came first (3)
4 Picture clue
5 Log off from dialogue, about to say farewell (5)
6 Picture clue
10 Picture clue
12 In-between insect said to be volcanic? (5)
13 How a ferry has on board a thin index (5)
15 Forego conclusion to find self (3)

ACROSS

1a. Certification (10)

9a. Rude about the lady! (1,3,2,5)

11a. "Bless my soul!" (3,2,6)

16a. Hopefully, it's impervious (4,6)

DOWN

1d. Where they ding dong merrily on high (10)

4d. Diplomatic (7)

6d. Trussed, so to speak... (10)

10d. What the new shop does (5,2)

PUZZLE 43

PITCHERWITS 3

ACROSS

1 Picture clue

5 Picture clue

8 Danish leader seen about requirements (5)

9 Herb said to be a great healer (5)

10 Fairly completely - take your pick (5)

12 Eradication, not at once for Circle Lines (5)

14 Picture clue

15 Picture clue

DOWN

1 Picture clue

2 Make foolish, when saddled centrally (5)

3 Written piece from SA (allegedly!) (5)

4 Picture clue

6 Picture clue

7 Picture clue

11 Delia's recipe - perfect! (5)

13 Doggone it - it's a bit quiet! (5)

ACROSS

1a. From walker to horse (7,4)

5a. Welsh/Polish aerials? (7)

14a. Useful for bad singer! (7)

15a. Bucket and spade feeling (7,4)

DOWN

1d. Cordial that's a tight fit? (5,6)

4d. On moral high-ground? (5-6)

6d. Louis - the milkman? (7)

7d. The actual answer is... (7)

PITCHERWITS 3

ACROSS

1 Picture clue
5 Scooter with a bit of bird noise (3)
6 Ooh! (Maybe it's a bit of resistance) (3)
7 Picture clue
10 No-one sounds like her - she's religious (3)
11 Any dope could set up this for public inspection (4,3)
12 Called, and at last showed the way (3)
13 Picture clue
16 Hebridean island said to have a yolk (3)
17 Layer of apprehension... (3)
18 Picture clue

DOWN

1 Picture clue
2 Custom built, in cemetery (4)
3 Opposed to, in the meantime... (4)
4 Picture clue
5 Picture clue
8 Main nerve-centre has a ring road (5)
9 Picture clue
14 Old villain, reputedly in church (4)
15 Even so, one is abominable (4)

ACROSS

1a. 'Plumptious' tart chemical? (5,4)

7a. "What's the...?" (3,4)

13a. The countryside - on stage? (7)

18a. Make up your own answer! (4,5)

DOWN

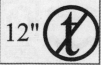
1d. Sound from drum kit's bass? (8)

4d. Said to have plain faces... 10 (10)

5d. Happens in billiards (7,3)

9d. It's not unnatural to have illumination (8)

PITCHERWITS 3

ACROSS

1 Picture clue
5 Rode around 5, - and took the car (5)
7 Budge over - get rid of glitches (5)
9 Picture clue
11 Shocking lie! (For a prophet!) (3)
12 Early singing? It's wicked! (3)
13 Picture clue
16 Retakes - but not at the back somehow - stinks! (5)
17 Risen from the ashes of water-wash (5)
18 Picture clue

DOWN

1 Picture clue
2 Refer to being less restricted (5)
3 Long, raised strip is something of a dirge (5)
4 Picture clue
6 Picture clue
8 Picture clue
10 Mother's ruin, in the beginning (3)
14 In church, say what you intend... (5)
15 Lob - it's most of value from below (5)

ACROSS

1a. Progress (4,7)

9a. Biggest answer yet! (7)

13a. Tiny, tiny, tiny amount (7)

18a. What the poorly paid need (6,5)

DOWN

1d. Hobbit world (6,5)

4d. Can they pick a winning hound? (3,8)

6d. What's your angle? (7)

8d. Would like to be a big hitter (7)

PITCHERWITS 3

ACROSS

1 Picture clue
7 Anger management is a cooker (5)
8 Picture clue
11 With ear to environmental bit of centre (5)
13 Met to design emblem (5)
14 Picture clue
16 Atlas type is masculine - twice (2-3)
18 Picture clue

DOWN

2 Grass bristle growing in lawns (3)
3 Picture clue
4 Dam - strange with dead end! (4)
5 Picture clue
6 Picture clue
9 Picture clue
10 Leave out of my inclusive talk initially (4)
12 Perched on circus tent (4)
15 Bead-work in retirement (4)
17 Emaciated piece of coat! (3)

ACROSS

1a. Beer with a punch (6,4)

8a. (Answer in secret) (3,4)

14a. Antelope jumpers (7)

18a. Bedspread to light? (10)

DOWN

3d. ...so you look to be asleep (3,5)

5d. Hill, but artificial (10)

6d. Forever picking holes (4,6)

9d. For marine exhibitionists? (4,4)

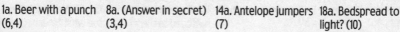

PITCHERWITS 3

ACROSS

1 Picture clue

5 Picture clue

8 Nice way in for my brother's child (5)

9 It's been due to give in (5)

10 Owed - a word in your ear - bit of a stink (5)

12 Merit, to be brief (5)

14 Picture clue

15 Picture clue

13 Civil way to dress the military (5)

DOWN

1 Picture clue

2 Read the runes as hospital worker (5)

3 Out-of-step ideas are lukewarm (5)

4 Picture clue

6 Picture clue

7 Picture clue

11 Duo to try and exceed (5)

ACROSS

1a. What the old con. did (4,7)

5a. Lifts the head (5,2)

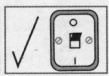

14a. Reprimand, clock switched to silent? (4,3)

15a. 'Unrustifying' (if you see what I mean) (11)

DOWN

1d. ...and write? (5,2,4)

4d. September night-shiner (7,4)

6d. That's fatty acid (7)

7d. Promise... (5,2)

PITCHERWITS 3

PUZZLE 48

ACROSS

1 Picture clue
5 Dog spotted in camera obscura (3)
6 Credited with a bit of colour (3)
7 Picture clue
10 Splits in half of the object (3)
11 Oaf tots dislike when over the limit (3,4)
12 Attention-holding number? (3)
13 Picture clue
16 Grief said to halt the horse (3)
17 Starting out with little bird (3)
18 Picture clue

DOWN

1 Picture clue
2 Froth of sounds on/off (4)
3 All a vast piece of magma (4)
4 Picture clue
5 Picture clue
8 Cheap meat of faltering content (5)
9 Picture clue
14 A positive sign - just as well! (4)
15 Sheep loose in Crewe Station (4)

ACROSS

1a. Attacked - with a condiment? (9)

7a. Put-you-up (4,3)

13a. Plead to take on board the little frog (7)

18a. Continues to stick with pressure? (7,2)

DOWN

1d. ...for being drunk and disorderly? (8)

4d. Contemptuous (10)

5d. It's a cartoon - on paper (5,5)

9d. Continue to struggle (6,2)

PITCHERWITS 3

ACROSS

1 Picture clue
5 Picture clue
7 Gel scraped off plumages for mountain lions (5)
8 Peak of Milligan? (5)
9 Eyepiece at hospital for whiskey (5)
11 Magnetics sent out for sorcery (5)
12 Picture clue
13 Picture clue

DOWN

1 Picture clue
2 Wombats? Not at where we came from (5)
3 Coins struck for the pictures (5)
4 Picture clue
5 Picture clue
6 Picture clue
10 Hippocratic Oath's reference to water horse (5)
11 Tum, if treated, can be civilly dressed (5)

ACROSS

1a. Could be cursive (11)

5a. Begin - from diving board? (4,3)

12a. If Prof's mistakes, then they're scams! (3-4)

13a. Scent away by these (11)

DOWN

1d. Manually brushed (4-7)

4d. Topping for blondie? (6,5)

5d. More edgy (7)

6d. They're cool! (7)

PITCHERWITS 3

ACROSS

1 Picture clue
5 Picture clue
9 Wander about but ram nothing in (4)
10 Deadly river has a twiggy sound (4)
11 Beginner to chat about door closer (5)
12 Highest point came to be (4)
14 Inform William he's the overture (4)
15 Picture clue
18 Picture clue

DOWN

1 Picture clue
2 Picture clue
3 Obliged to hear a poem (3)
4 Make music to trap the bird (3)
6 Bad dictators lose account of twist (7)
7 How to treat the little I's? (3)
8 Picture clue
10 Picture clue
13 Talking bull? - a bit smooth! (3)
16 Sorbet will not set as a ball (3)
17 Chop suey's for her! (3)

ACROSS

1a. Melon (sort of) (10)

5a. This bit's extra! (8)

15a. It's a threshold thing (8)

18a. Fracture fixer (10)

DOWN

1d. Pack picture... (5,4)

2d. Squash (not orange!) (7)

8d. Cheeky Chappie! (3,6)

10d. Hut opts out of being field event (4,3)

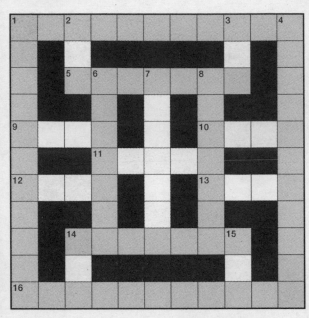

ACROSS

1 Picture clue
5 Picture clue
9 One-ten lives as a centre (4)
10 Perched on some circus tent (4)
11 Vagrant to begin trampolining (5)
12 Double act - is a dead duck? (4)
13 Lots to make for TV section (4)
14 Picture clue
16 Picture clue

DOWN

1 Picture clue
2 Fired in anger (3)
3 Doers or not, little Desmond? (3)
4 Picture clue
6 Picture clue
7 Babe caused loss of evil on account of being (7)
8 Picture clue
14 Bit of research that's not straight? (3)
15 Alpine travel in one's kid gloves (3)

ACROSS

1a. Feature that's a bay watch? (5,6)

5a. These are for eating (7)

14a. Goes to (7)

16a. Acknowledgement (11)

DOWN

1d. More repeats... (4,3,4)

4d. Way to greet at a distance? (4,7)

6d. Deform (7)

8d. Passed by (7)

PITCHERWITS 3

ACROSS

1 Picture clue
6 Values us - outside the valley (4)
7 Cowsay to solve... (Eh? What's a cowsay?) (3)
8 Envisage something of an entry permit (4)
9 Picture clue
11 Picture clue
14 Such atmospheres to talk in (4)
15 Beat - somewhat annoying (3)
16 Prima donna - she's right greedy! (4)
17 Picture clue

DOWN

1 Picture clue
2 Picture clue
3 Lock rests in confusion (5)
4 Ambusher - he's out for the odd dance! (5)
5 Picture clue
10 Picture clue
12 He'll sing for ten quid, they say (5)
13 Aidan comes up to her (5)

ACROSS

1a. Intensive, creative thinking (10)

9a. Steady now! (8)

11a. Verbally, they're opposite (8)

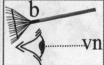

17a. Makes no profit - or loss (6,4)

DOWN

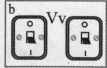

1d. They live all right! (3,7)

2d. It's empty of Latin (2,5)

5d. Rifle, kind of (4-6)

10d. Proportional (2,5)

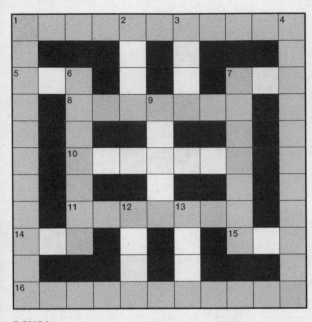

ACROSS

1 Picture clue
5 Take in half a breath (3)
7 It starts out as ribonucleic acid (1,1,1)
8 Picture clue
10 How the climber repeatedly gets there? (2,3,2)
11 Picture clue
14 Disapproval of eggs in Rome (3)
15 Put on University type (3)
16 Picture clue

DOWN

1 Picture clue
2 Grave place to end up! (4)
3 I said, in Greece... (4)
4 Picture clue
6 Picture clue
7 Picture clue
9 Argument to enter at speed (3-2)
12 Deli product? Plain lazy! (4)
13 'Medal' struck before dinner? (4)

ACROSS

1a. Where posh drinks are served? (8,3)

8a. Hug (7)

11a. Having extra long retirement? (5,2)

16a. For small gap measuring (6,5)

DOWN

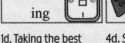

1d. Taking the best (8,3)

4d. Support with confidence (11)

6d. ...quite messy to the French (7)

7d. React (7)

ACROSS

1 Picture clue
5 Picture clue
9 Be aware, it sounds like a refusal (4)
10 Nation in/out of this security group (4)
11 Run back in, that is, to harden (5)
12 "Hey, be quiet in court!" (4)
14 Avid about the prima donna (4)
15 Picture clue
18 Picture clue

DOWN

1 Picture clue
2 Picture clue
3 Sense of humour, described as whiskey (3)
4 Brushed out for that lady (3)
6 Peanut I digest as a flower (7)
7 One's party – held in Bath? (3)
8 Picture clue
10 Picture clue
13 You sound sheepish! (3)
16 Deferrals, containing mistake (3)
17 Ocean said to be in bishop's turf (3)

ACROSS

1a. Is it stationery? (5,5)

5a. The answer costs? (8)

15a. Experience security (4,4)

18a. Nothing else matters... (10)

DOWN

1d. Started, on pitch (6,3)

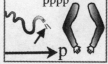

2d. Aw gosh! (3,4)

8d. Lean those guns! (5,4)

10d. Roosevelt policy (3,4)

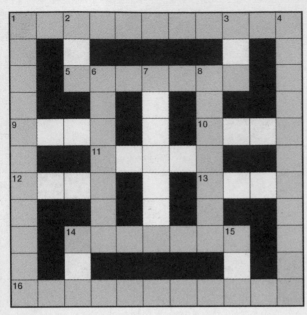

ACROSS

1 Picture clue

5 Picture clue

9 Emit, in a way, a bit of a list (4)

10 It's later, bluntly - author unknown (4)

11 Strings for a mummy's boy (5)

12 Club for (and from) greens (4)

13 High speed panache? (4)

14 Picture clue

16 Picture clue

DOWN

1 Picture clue

2 Amicably discovered a taxi (3)

3 Purpose that's half obtuse (3)

4 Picture clue

6 Picture clue

7 Orpheus produces prop job (5,2)

8 Picture clue

14 Level (twice) of sparring partner (3)

15 Cape gooseberry has own identity (3)

ACROSS

1a. Rubbish story! (4,3,4)

5a. Curt (7)

14a. Give it a blow? (3,4)

16a. It could make one rich (5,6)

DOWN

1d. Depending on... (11)

4d. Conserve (5,6)

6d. Balkan place (7)

8d. Whizkid progress (2,3,2)

PITCHERWITS 3

ACROSS

1 Picture clue

7 Picture of game I designed (5)

8 Homespun duet's not warranted (5)

9 Picture clue

11 Picture clue

14 Nip on transport to attach blame (3,2)

15 Colour said to unlock motor (5)

16 Picture clue

DOWN

1 Picture clue

2 Call a man about a little woolly camel (5)

3 Have to pay in the flowerpot (3)

4 Picture clue

5 Make sense – totally? (3,2)

6 Picture clue

10 Picture clue

12 Insurance without cars? Could produce boredom (5)

13 Amino compound from the Arab world (5)

15 It's most important to unlock... (3)

ACROSS

1a. Principle of a chemist (7,3)

9a. Approaching (7,2,2)

11a. Highly delighted (4,3,4)

16a. So, not ahead then? (4,2,4)

DOWN

1d. Parade ground group (5,5)

4d. Import – that's illegal! (7)

6d. Gives you in-flight power (4,6)

10d. That's acute! (7)

PITCHERWITS 3

ACROSS

1 Picture clue

5 Picture clue

8 Rose has got a point (5)

9 Louse treatment for bird (5)

10 Question said to come fourth (5)

12 Sees a way, and alleviates (5)

14 Picture clue

15 Picture clue

DOWN

1 Picture clue
2 Short-term worker has no pace (5)
3 Affirms the saver's in trouble (5)
4 Picture clue
6 Picture clue
7 Picture clue
11 Walsh's pattern of shoulder cloak (5)
13 Eve is back in front of the strainer (5)

ACROSS

1a. Computer's maternal bit? (11)

5a. Now there's the rub... (7)

14a. Greatly impressive answer! (7)

15a. Keep back (4,2,5)

DOWN

1d. Rowan (not a horse!) (8,3)

4d. Returns (could be sneaky!) (7,4)

6d. Genuine Pitcherwits answer (7)

7d. No second attempt... (2,3,2)

PITCHERWITS 3

ACROSS

1 Picture clue
5 Bit inaccurate for a dog... (3)
6 How a crow fancies his mate? (3)
7 Picture clue
10 It's said to be sod's, but it's statute! (3)
11 Feeler has a worker to back the queen (7)
12 How deer get in the groove? (3)
13 Picture clue
16 Bar from some introductions (3)
17 Tea store is burnt out (3)
18 Picture clue

DOWN

1 Picture clue
2 Latest of all directions (4)
3 It's that hideous fruit again! (4)
4 Picture clue
5 Picture clue
8 Glee I discovered in feudal allegiance (5)
9 Picture clue
14 Upward raffle (4)
15 Artist maybe, but tedious with it? (4)

ACROSS

1a. Got nothing on the French! (2,7)

7a. Trick of the hand (small, say) (7)

13a. Bad act (7)

18a. ...plans, perhaps? (7,2)

DOWN

1d. Sometimes under trains... (8)

4d. When leaves fell (4,6)

5d. Remember? (4,2,4)

9d. ...and ready to go (6,2)

ACROSS

1 Picture clue
5 Niger mapped out for rule (5)
7 Misdirect aid in Asian republic (5)
9 Picture clue
11 One in Westminster is a little devil (3)
12 Tiny Scots and sweet? No way! (3)
13 Picture clue
16 Produce of high calibre education (5)
17 Back at the front, it's a letter to a Greek (5)
18 Picture clue

DOWN

1 Picture clue
2 Old plastic, but still a record (5)
3 Tunis - in poor shape for singles (5)
4 Picture clue
6 Picture clue
8 Picture clue
10 I'm a bit categorical... (3)
14 Circle lines not on Underground maps (5)
15 Sort of violet that's extreme? (5)

ACROSS

1a. How the central European jumped? (4-7)

9a. Liaises somehow in Poland (7)

13a. Drafty state? (2,5)

18a. Test for you! (11)

DOWN

1d. You can surely see this? (11)

4d. Positive about this one? (4,7)

6d. Encourage within church edifice (7)

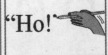

8d. Weedy weed cutter (4,3)

PITCHERWITS 3

ACROSS

1 Picture clue

7 Coin I struck atomically? (5)

8 Picture clue

11 Meals said to be a bit of a leg-pull (5)

13 Anglers (without generalising) can produce jinns (5)

14 Picture clue

16 Get in! (Somehow colour slightly) (5)

18 Picture clue

DOWN

2 Wan sort of grass bristle (3)

3 Picture clue

4 Automobile sort of edict? (4)

5 Picture clue

6 Picture clue

9 Picture clue

10 Me to scam, say, the legend (4)

12 Resting on single T-shirt (4)

15 Engrave, in wretched surroundings (4)

17 Catch that's not gross, allegedly (3)

ACROSS

1a. Charming - that's lucky (6,4)

8a. Touchy-feely answer (7)

14a. Level charges (7)

18a. Do they sell hosiery here? (5,5)

DOWN

3d. Bugs (but not bunny) (8)

5d. Office equipment - going back some! (10)

6d. What Esau sold off cheap (10)

9d. Entangled (6,2)

PITCHERWITS 3

ACROSS

1 Picture clue

5 Picture clue

8 Tick over, etc, gone but reset in Russian town (5)

9 Of the kidneys, it's to learn about (5)

10 They're dummies (code!) (5)

12 Cocoons, but not on these islands (5)

14 Picture clue

15 Picture clue

DOWN

1 Picture clue

2 Riviera town on the river is more pleasant (5)

3 Connect with edition - do not muddle (3,2)

4 Picture clue

6 Picture clue

7 Picture clue

11 Out of Plymouth comes body fluid (5)

13 About to join member for ascent (5)

ACROSS

1a. Just built (11)

5a. Hag-laugh, right in the fire noise (7)

14a. Drink on the train I'm about to get (7)

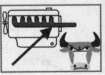

15a. It can be worn - out (11)

DOWN

1d. To keep the layers contained (7,4)

4d. Between the lines... (6,5)

6d. Drive, as if crazy expert helper (7)

7d. Non-alcoholic port - it's in Pakistan (7)

PITCHERWITS 3

ACROSS

1 Picture clue
5 Feathery reptile? (3)
6 Where it's all at when muddled (3)
7 Picture clue
10 By hook or by crook, it's got the ball (3)
11 Advance to better software! (7)
12 Bath floating in cyberspace (3)
13 Picture clue
16 Time of geranium cutting (3)
17 Article? Definitely! (3)
18 Picture clue

DOWN

1 Picture clue
2 Subtle approach hides a jump (4)
3 They're strange for bookies? (4)
4 Picture clue
5 Picture clue
8 Informally greet heron (5)
9 Picture clue
14 Almost not to be given to the poor! (4)
15 A one about age... (4)

ACROSS

1a. Complete eat-sleep package (4,5)

7a. Opens, in order to provide cash (7)

13a. Java (not script) place (7)

18a. Just being yourself? (9)

DOWN

1d. Quick money (4,4)

4d. Comic in a frock (5,2,3)

5d. Laughable, but not that funny (3,2,1,4)

9d. Dance - sub-zero? (3,5)

PUZZLE 63

ACROSS

1 Picture clue
5 Picture clue
7 Style of painting has no section (2,3)
8 Unfamiliar road I take to be medium (5)
9 Dualist is not about to be grown up (5)
11 Decorate radon dispersion (5)
12 Picture clue
13 Picture clue

DOWN

1 Picture clue
2 Designed art - it's a characteristic (5)
3 Ravel composition - like soft palate! (5)
4 Picture clue
5 Picture clue
6 Picture clue
10 Add (that's your lot)! (5)
11 Honour to be found in hospital section (5)

ACROSS

1a. Atom? Positively not! (8,3)

5a. Mega-clucking state (2,1,4)

12a. It's pegged in (not out) (3,4)

13a. Rotary rumba, say? (6,5)

DOWN

1d. 30-year old pop music (3,8)

4d. Arrival (7,4)

5d. Speedy eh? (2,1,4)

6d. Hoarse Plaice, say? (7)

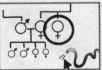

PITCHERWITS 3

ACROSS

1 Picture clue
5 Picture clue
9 Agreement squashed in, allegedly (4)
10 Avon's star, seen from right angle (4)
11 Conjure up artless take-over plan (5)
12 Soup recipe is quite a work (4)
14 Reign with a straight edge? (4)
15 Picture clue
18 Picture clue

DOWN

1 Picture clue
2 Picture clue
3 Antelope gun goes off (3)
4 Pelt with some tofu recipes (3)
6 She's a nation in trouble! (7)
7 I'm a bit woebegone myself (3)
8 Picture clue
10 Picture clue
13 Geller - a bit amateurish! (3)
16 Always (once in the Bayeux tapestry) (3)
17 Court wooden half (3)

ACROSS

1a. Getting less... (7,3)

5a. Gustave - France's best novelist? (8)

15a. What every worker should have (4,4)

18a. Just meets... (10)

DOWN

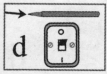
1d. Warned (6,3)

2d. They could be socialists (7)

8d. Work rests (3,6)

10d. Dearest partner... (7)

PUZZLE 65

PITCHERWITS 3

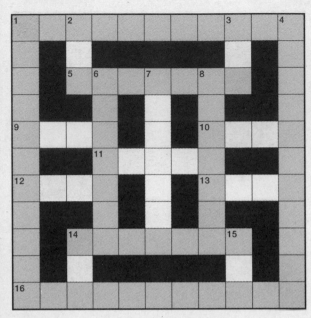

ACROSS

1 Picture clue
5 Picture clue
9 Operation has no ratio to start (4)
10 Bookrack - store for veg. (4)
11 Trees shredded for organic compound (5)
12 Sour sort, belonging to us (4)
13 Had a lesson in the valley (4)
14 Picture clue
16 Picture clue

DOWN

1 Picture clue
2 Nothing extracted from vanilla (3)
3 Pull from the belltower (3)
4 Picture clue
6 Picture clue
7 Irresponsibly ignited eating habits (7)
8 Picture clue
14 The edge of acrimony (3)
15 Friskier bit of Alpine travel (3)

ACROSS

1a. It's not sticky! (3-8)

5a. ...by the 'flu, maybe (4,3)

14a. Forest people (7)

16a. It had a rise and fall (5,6)

DOWN

1d. Avoid overdoing it (3,2,3,3)

4d. What a soupy answer! (4-1-6)

6d. Now, what was that answer? Er... (7)

8d. Not in the shop just yet (2,5)

PITCHERWITS 3

ACROSS

1 Picture clue
6 The sort of skull that can be operated on? (4)
7 Teachers' address - goodnight, say? (3)
8 Man skirt left in kit (4)
9 Picture clue
11 Picture clue
14 Haul around the dance (4)
15 Sweet, but no way is it tiny (3)
16 Ostentatious bit of a dwelling... (4)
17 Picture clue

DOWN

1 Picture clue
2 Picture clue
3 Fine and notable, but at a loss (5)
4 Relieves beasties, but a bit put out (5)
5 Picture clue
10 Picture clue
12 Mediocre doctrine to give beliefs (5)
13 Edit tons of bits of copy, Mark (5)

ACROSS

1a. Slushy finance? (10)

9a. Angers (8)

11a. Settling on (8)

17a. Lose it - totally (2,2,6)

DOWN

1d. Gave in - vertically? (6,4)

2d. Raft of explorations (3-4)

5d. They're a sight! (5,5)

10d. Dark clothing? (7)

PITCHERWITS 3

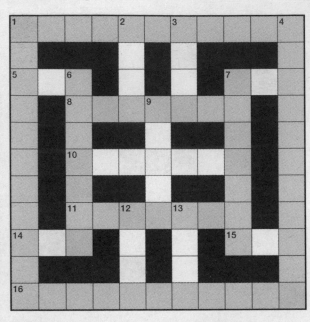

ACROSS

1 Picture clue
5 Smirking can somewhat irritate (3)
7 Not many are said to smell this bad! (3)
8 Picture clue
10 GNP item could be for colour (7)
11 Picture clue
14 Objection heard from the goat? (3)
15 Hill going back to decay (3)
16 Picture clue

DOWN

1 Picture clue
2 Tight angle to trap taste in (4)
3 Doer about to treat again (4)
4 Picture clue
6 Picture clue
7 Picture clue
9 Humdrum ballet in centre-dance (5)
12 Competition man (4)
13 Limit of audible roadside (4)

ACROSS

1a. Look about right (5,6)

8a. Chinese dish with spinning shell? (3,4)

11a. Fear a checkmate – bit of a pain (7)

16a. It just shows you how competitors are! (11)

DOWN

1d. By gum, it's fixed! (6,5)

4d. When morale has plummeted (11)

6d. Where the angler has success? (7)

7d. Praise - more on the level? (7)

PITCHERWITS 3

ACROSS

1 Picture clue

5 Picture clue

9 Eastern sages of some imagination (4)

10 Prey destroyed by funeral fire (4)

11 A loss, adjusted (for ropey answer!) (5)

12 Be defeated by sloe cocktail (4)

14 Engrave - in ketchup? (4)

15 Picture clue

18 Picture clue

DOWN

1 Picture clue
2 Picture clue
3 Former piece of bold font (3)
4 Actions of the disc operating system (3)

6 Learning points - from the lectern? (7)
7 It's policy to be half frozen (3)
8 Picture clue
10 Picture clue

13 Water travel - as kings do, partly (3)
16 Spiders' work in www (3)
17 Indian province, several changes ago (3)

ACROSS

1a. Yliad (not Homer's) (5,5)

5a. For 100,000 albums (4,4)

15a. Visits en route (6,2)

18a. ...like the unserviced car (6,4)

DOWN

1d. Sounds like introductions... (4,5)

2d. This can be read (7)

8d. Naughty but so nice (5,4)

10d. Surprised - like cartoon Olive? (3-4)

PITCHERWITS 3

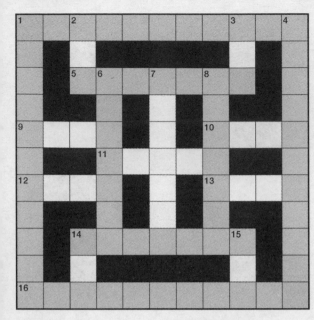

ACROSS

1 Picture clue

5 Picture clue

9 Hide anxiety in a concept (4)

10 Grid to be found in game shop (4)

11 "Chew noisily," said little Victor (5)

12 Shrubby sort of president? (4)

13 Singing or flying, you're alone (4)

14 Picture clue

16 Picture clue

DOWN

1 Picture clue

2 Formerly looked up (3)

3 First Lady, at some level (3)

4 Picture clue

6 Picture clue

7 Totally regrets the basil we cooked (7)

8 Picture clue

14 Classy title? (3)

15 Grateful of it for the tree? (3)

ACROSS

1a. Just before 2016 (or 2017...) (3,5,3)

5a. After the corn harvest - could it be designer? (7)

14a. It's fruity! (7)

16a. Would he/she educate a bench? (4,7)

DOWN

1d. Shortly, it'll be the latest (4,2,5)

4d. Basically, she's fertile (5,6)

5d. Breathing space? (7)

9d. Cash at, say, 65 (4,3)

PITCHERWITS 3

ACROSS

1 Picture clue
7 Entrance to apply political pressure? (5)
8 Tip me over to get music speeds (5)
9 Picture clue
11 Picture clue
14 A rope, knotted for musical item (5)
15 Doctor's one in a million with throw of dice (5)
16 Picture clue

DOWN

1 Picture clue
2 Ban scant thanks with a jeer (5)
3 Narrative song for hen do? (3)
4 Picture clue
5 Small part of brooch (5)
6 Picture clue
10 Picture clue
12 Three put in that place (5)
13 Led on deviously in these days (5)
15 Two-way, silent producer? (3)

ACROSS

1a. Is it straitened? (10)

9a. How Henry found Becket (11)

11a. BRRRH! (7,4)

16a. Postponements (10)

DOWN

1d. Sad one in the scale of things (1,4,5)

4d. Absent (3,4)

6d. Quilted fliers? (5,5)

10d. Group time - used to dress wound? (7)

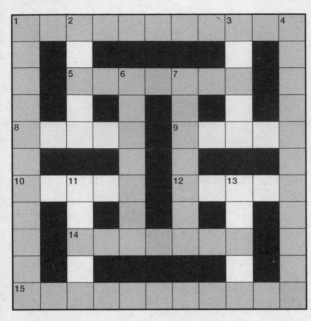

ACROSS

1 Picture clue

5 Picture clue

8 Automaton to rob with violence (5)

9 Not the best two-star, not at this setting (5)

10 Mike - stony sort of fighter (5)

12 Deduce the finer details (5)

14 Picture clue

15 Picture clue

DOWN

1 Picture clue

2 Bush is so much plush rubbish! (5)

3 Either way, it's a detection system (5)

4 Picture clue

6 Picture clue

7 Picture clue

11 Not to be sniffed at - or is it? (5)

13 Falsified sort of sweet? (5)

ACROSS

1a. None shall sleep - for a tenner, say? (6,5)

5a. What Atlas' muscles did? (7)

14a. Yet to come... (2,5)

15a. Claim of content (4,2,5)

DOWN

1d. Follow it in the woods, perhaps? (6,5)

4d. Just very popular actors... (3-4,4)

6d. Ape unit built as flower (7)

7d. When blue water feels blue? (3,4)

PITCHERWITS 3

ACROSS

1 Picture clue
5 Two, assiduously pruned (3)
6 Catty son of a piper (3)
7 Picture clue
10 Sounds surprising, either way (3)
11 Outshine Eve's sides, including paper holders (7)
12 Spot Ruskin in snow travel (3)
13 Picture clue
16 Two changes to pull (3)
17 Washed-out tree (3)
18 Picture clue

DOWN

1 Picture clue
2 They stick your teeth in? (4)
3 Grown right out of the dress (4)
4 Picture clue
5 Picture clue
8 Turn of events at the disco (5)
9 Picture clue
14 Gemstone that one can get tired of? (4)
15 Irish dish gone west (4)

ACROSS

1a. Twisty (9)

7a. Comedian just won't sit down (5-2)

13a. Burner features (3,4)

18a. Wings it (5,4)

DOWN

1d. ...and cross the t's (3,3,1'1)

4d. Crochet move (4,6)

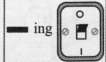

5d. Getting away quickly - with hyphens? (7,3)

9d. Peter's out? (4,4)

ACROSS

1 Picture clue
5 Chose unlikely depot for solution (5)
7 Confess, and allow in (5)
9 Picture clue
11 Before the real pieces (3)
12 Males that are a bit demented! (3)
13 Picture clue
16 I will, I said, be part of the church (5)
17 It's very musical! (5)
18 Picture clue

DOWN

1 Picture clue
2 Give final, painful cry (5)
3 Conscious of a weak organisation (5)
4 Picture clue
6 Picture clue
8 Picture clue
10 Ban all the legal types (3)
14 Firestone is not soft for her (5)
15 Roach, cooked for salty veg. (5)

ACROSS

1a. This is an old one! (11)

9a. Dipped... (3,4)

13a. Kenyan city in a biro accident (7)

18a. Big tipple! (5,6)

DOWN

1d. Aim to hoop it (7,4)

4d. Which is your country? (11)

6d. Gifts (7)

8d. They're dead old, these Egyptians (7)

PITCHERWITS 3

ACROSS

1 Picture clue

7 Grasp a standard piece of spaghetti, say (5)

8 Picture clue

11 Theatre business - bit of a puzzle (5)

13 Cot is reshaped for the old school (5)

14 Picture clue

16 Take a cent, in order to perform (5)

18 Picture clue

DOWN

2 Bit of eyeshadow? Affirmative! (3)

3 Picture clue

4 All I'm bothered about is a leg, say (4)

5 Picture clue

6 Picture clue

9 Picture clue

10 Up and down spinner repeating (2-2)

12 Ordered as hounds howled, say (4)

15 A way out of perplexity (4)

17 Melody heard on broadcasting (3)

ACROSS

1a. Staring at... (10)

8a. Farewells (3-4)

14a. Cat, with dishonest reputation (7)

18a. Strong drinkers? (10)

DOWN

3d. Don't attend (2,6)

5d. Returns (not many happy) (4,4,2)

6d. Neared (10)

9d. It's a case of yolk.... (8)

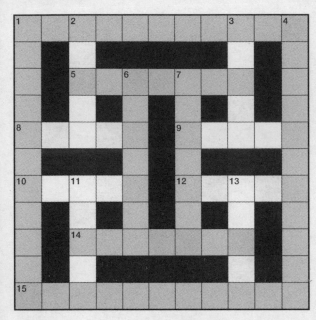

ACROSS

1 Picture clue

5 Picture clue

8 Line I take to be the rest (3-2)

9 Shaken duo to do better (5)

10 About an excess of protection.... (5)

12 Soft instrument? (5)

14 Picture clue

15 Picture clue

DOWN

1 Picture clue

2 Said to project spasm of pain (5)

3 Call in at six, and park yourself (5)

4 Picture clue

6 Picture clue

7 Picture clue

11 'Visitors, it's not to be looked through' (5)

13 Goodbye! (At last!) (5)

ACROSS

1a. One for the birds and the bees? (6,5)

5a. What goes around... (7)

14a. Warrior (7)

15a. Huge chunk (5,6)

DOWN

1d. Where to contemplate a tum? (5,6)

4d. Designed to backfire (11)

6d. Turn mat over for a bout of temper (7)

7d. Military index of swearing? (7)

PITCHERWITS 3

ACROSS

1 Picture clue
5 Go down - with sauce! (3)
6 Second letter add-on... (1,1,1)
7 Picture clue
10 Tor excavated for its mineral (3)
11 Chap is, I think somehow, a board game (7)
12 In truth, it is a groove... (3)
13 Picture clue
16 Some prophet to be made from Bakelite... (3)
17 'Maiden name' needed in first half (3)
18 Picture clue

DOWN

1 Picture clue
2 Fracas happily contained - in purse, say? (4)
3 Plunging in breathing aid (4)
4 Picture clue
5 Picture clue
8 Either I leave, or there's an atmosphere (5)
9 Picture clue
14 An idiot thing to do to the cream! (4)
15 "Darling, that's expensive..." (4)

ACROSS

1a. Stuck in the heat.... (3,6)

7a. Talking of being weary... (5-2)

13a. Prompt sort of sign (3,4)

18a. Don't look in it's mouth! (4,5)

DOWN

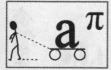
1d. Sweet order? (5,3)

4d. Lofting fellow (2,8)

5d. Branding as bad (10)

9d. Crack, sort of (8)

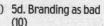

PITCHERWITS 3

ACROSS

1 Picture clue
5 Picture clue
7 Deaf around May 1st, but well-known (5)
8 Heaths situated in backroom, from September (5)
9 Provide with a virtual joke? (5)
11 Cloth dug out backwards (5)
12 Picture clue
13 Picture clue

DOWN

1 Picture clue
2 Save up what the donkey half-said? (5)
3 Aim to put ox back into familiar saying (5)
4 Picture clue
5 Picture clue
6 Picture clue
10 Pro I'm taking to be double top (5)
11 Finger the old rocker might be keen on? (5)

ACROSS

1a. Coupling (11)

5a. Perceiving (7)

12a. What lift might be doing (5,2)

13a. ...to a good friend (4,2,5)

DOWN

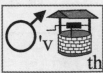

1d. He's 'got a bob or two' (3,2,9)

4d. Revolting quantity? (5,6)

5d. It's on the Elbe (7)

6d. Adult vertical reaction, say, to a pun? (5,2)

PITCHERWITS 3

ACROSS

1. Picture clue
5. Picture clue
9. Tidy - in one attempt (4)
10. Tiniest piece of moat is dug (4)
11. Little summary in there, Captain (5)
12. What a lazy engine does? (4)
14. Scowl - with flourish - when fish hooked (4)
15. Picture clue
18. Picture clue

DOWN

1. Picture clue
2. Picture clue
3. Curvy bit of research? (3)
4. Viewed from inside, she's a woolly one (3)
6. Picnic spoiled round turn for opera man (7)
7. Kitchen-starting gear (3)
8. Picture clue
10. Picture clue
13. Galileo finally got a constellation! (3)
16. This old Roman - drunk? (3)
17. Snake - in the airing-cupboard! (3)

ACROSS

1a. You can bin it! (10)

5a. Dainties (8)

15a. White Nile stork (8)

18a. Are they exhausting for cars? (10)

DOWN

1d. First light attacks (4,5)

2d. Icon (7)

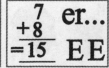
8d. In nutshells? (9)

10d. NASA's moonmobiles? (7)

ACROSS

1 Picture clue

5 Picture clue

9 Be at odds to help (4)

10 Finally acknowledge the limit (4)

11 Pouches somehow lose us time (5)

12 Doom to Hell (but hold the water, say) (4)

13 Crude cure - it's beige (4)

14 Picture clue

16 Picture clue

DOWN

1 Picture clue

2 She's a producer, up and down (3)

3 Admired a bit of anger (3)

4 Picture clue

6 Picture clue

7 A nation in trouble? That's her! (7)

8 Picture clue

14 After after-thought in the post (1,1,1)

15 Oil platform? It's a set-up! (3)

ACROSS

1a. Banned at Westminster (believe it or not!) (4-7)

5a. Sickness of a double crooked smile (7)

14a. Fuss (7)

16a. What a dieter does (or hopes to)! (5,6)

DOWN

1d. How a lager should be (4,3,4)

4d. Punch, say (5,6)

6d. Does it have an aerial view? (7)

8d. Now listen... (3,4)

PITCHERWITS 3

ACROSS

1 Picture clue
6 Help to make one gamble (4)
7 Eggs sounding like they're done (3)
8 Wicked to go back live (4)
9 Picture clue
11 Picture clue
14 A. G.'s final ringer (4)
15 Percentage needing a plaster? (3)
16 Care about part of the region (4)
17 Picture clue

DOWN

1 Picture clue
2 Picture clue
3 It's everything musical... (5)
4 Romps around formal balls (5)
5 Picture clue
10 Picture clue
12 Text 'Racing Snippets' for more... (5)
13 Fallacies - fell out about patriarch (5)

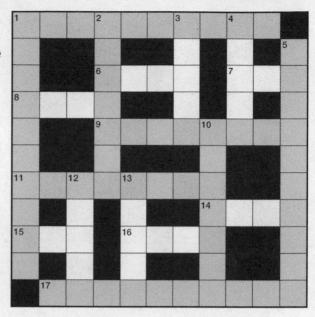

ACROSS

1a. ABC stuff (5,5)

9a. Outshone (8)

11a. Could be an iris (8)

17a. For the record, they're visual (10)

DOWN

1d. Charles de Gaulle people (4,6)

2d. Make it bigger (5,2)

5d. Sticky (X2) fairground stuff (10)

10d. Varicoloured (7)

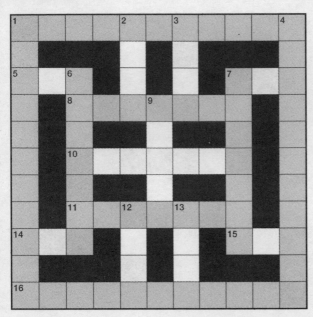

ACROSS

1 Picture clue
5 Roman road, in enviable postion (3)
7 Doctors club, back in Lambda (1,1,1)
8 Picture clue
10 Left paper in turbine - crazy! (7)
11 Picture clue
14 Police finally have the 'diamonds' (3)
15 Bird at reduced altitude (3)
16 Picture clue

DOWN

1 Picture clue
2 Ended in poverty (4)
3 Low tide - in one application (4)
4 Picture clue
6 Picture clue
7 Picture clue
9 Seem bedevilled somewhat by implant (5)
12 Responsibility is on us to join (4)
13 Libido hidden in same place - for Romans (4)

ACROSS

1a. Ignoring... (3,8)

8a. Not a response for this one! (2,5)

11a. More temperamental (7)

16a. Covered up (7,4)

DOWN

1d. He could be on board (5,6)

4d. Serious thing (5,6)

6d. Whenever... (7)

7d. Wrote, say (2,5)

PITCHERWITS 3

ACROSS

1 Picture clue
5 Picture clue
9 Just open one – of jam? (4)
10 He will inherit the sound of a melody (4)
11 Headgear Tara takes one in for (5)
12 Devil's work for these hands! (4)
14 Loud version of game (4)
15 Picture clue
18 Picture clue

DOWN

1 Picture clue
2 Picture clue
3 Beer said to make you poorly (3)
4 Flying force contained, after a fashion (1,1,1)
6 Aspirin dissolved for Ark boarding pattern (2,5)
7 Due to hear a poem (3)
8 Picture clue
10 Picture clue
13 Cleaner part of the meadow (3)
16 Spirit of selflessness (3)
17 Sick of millions being cut... (3)

ACROSS

1a. Appears wet in order to be binned (5,5)

5a. Gets less... (5,3)

15a. Comes to see (8)

18a. Goes to pieces (5,5)

DOWN

1d. Overstep the mark here - and get wet! (5,4)

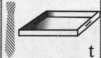

2d. Measure solution strength (7)

8d. Front area (9)

10d. Drags - vertically? (5,2)

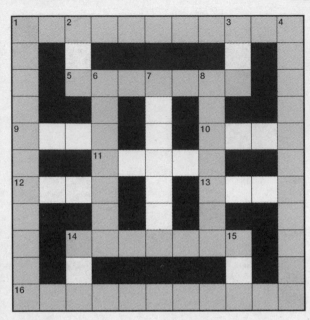

ACROSS

1 Picture clue

5 Picture clue

9 Craziest site, gone from odd Russian ruler (4)

10 Outvote the stoppage (4)

11 Concur, in meagre extract (5)

12 Tend to result in depression (4)

13 Song of Parliamentarian cutbacks (4)

14 Picture clue

16 Picture clue

DOWN

1 Picture clue

2 Rope formation sounds negative (3)

3 A piece of Spode - holding peas (3)

4 Picture clue

6 Picture clue

7 Set-fair, strangely, for best looking (7)

8 Picture clue

14 Star, relatively speaking (3)

15 Terrier is a bit of a stray (3)

ACROSS

1a. Where scrubbing's not needed (3-5,3)

5a. No Delft is designed this many times (7)

14a. How the beetle could sink the ship? (7)

16a. For pastures new? (4,7)

DOWN

1d. No names... for old army types (2,4,5)

4d. Would be a crime to mash them! (3,8)

6d. Unpredictable crater I went round (7)

8d. Romantic draw? (4,3)

PITCHERWITS 3

ACROSS

1 Picture clue

7 Rebel leader finished as a wanderer (5)

8 A change of heart, Mother, perhaps? (5)

9 Picture clue

11 Picture clue

14 Motherly, but lot less strange as nursery poem (5)

15 About ammo fired back at punctuation (5)

16 Picture clue

DOWN

1 Picture clue
2 Delve silently into hiding place for imps (5)
3 How to state differences atmospherically? (3)

4 Picture clue
5 Undergrowth to clean with? (5)
6 Picture clue
10 Picture clue
12 Season, say, for seasoning (5)

13 Ambusher - he's out for the odd dance (5)
15 Gear spotted incognito (3)

ACROSS

1a. Easy to get to... (4,6)

9a. Cannot be overcome (11)

11a. Put in, here and there (11)

16a. All a matter of degree... (10)

DOWN

1d. Strengtheners (10)

4d. Make happier (5,2)

6d. Now that's a pud! (10)

10d. Omen (7)

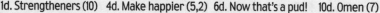

ACROSS

1 Picture clue

5 Picture clue

8 'Language' of the crazy log-in (5)

9 Terse sort of button (5)

10 Lure Euro member into races (5)

12 Seen as a latent bit of nose (5)

14 Picture clue

15 Picture clue

DOWN

1 Picture clue

2 An odd, strange extra (3-2)

3 Stood around for task list (2-3)

4 Picture clue

6 Picture clue

7 Picture clue

11 Army officer John, PM (5)

13 Spray in spring, say, with a cold? (5)

ACROSS

1a. Due to... (2,7,2)

5a. Ten-footer (7)

14a. Can flavour gin (7)

15a. Flat out (but not fast!) (11)

DOWN

1d. They're for all to read (4,7)

4d. Partly, it's brainy! (7,4)

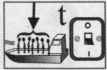

6d. Contour recipe is a soup extra (7)

7d. Pips ran all over the root veg. (7)

PITCHERWITS 3

PUZZLE 86

ACROSS

1 Picture clue
5 Slippery one from Darjeeling (3)
6 Tool that's said to have everything (3)
7 Picture clue
10 Request, while kickstarting (3)
11 Show reason for one-time flatland (7)
12 Boiling a bit of salad dressing (3)
13 Picture clue
16 Geller - a bit Arthurian (3)
17 Rest of mid-Wales, in other words (3)
18 Picture clue

DOWN

1 Picture clue
2 Steeply set out as a high-pitched cry (4)
3 In this way, can be a bit enthusiastic! (4)
4 Picture clue
5 Picture clue
8 Map man - with the world on his shoulders? (5)
9 Picture clue
14 Model won't go with Rolling Stone? (4)
15 Neurosis - it's got currency! (4)

ACROSS

1a. Geoffrey'd? (9)

7a. A slippy kind of thing in your wage packet (7)

13a. Bitty action? (7)

18a. Social uniform (5,4)

DOWN

1d. Shiner that doesn't? (5,3)

4d. Writes to (5,1,4)

5d. Understood (10)

9d. Said to be flawed (4,4)

ACROSS

1 Picture clue
5 Rot returns, so ending the trunk (5)
7 Pies - a recipe for light brown (5)
9 Picture clue
11 Mat taking back headgear (3)
12 M.P. - who has a plan! (3)
13 Picture clue
16 Tooting, but not to ruin block of metal (5)
17 Weird antic of muscle protein (5)
18 Picture clue

DOWN

1 Picture clue
2 Standoffish? Just one of us Loofs! (5)
3 Lanyards dry out and become sort of nosey (5)
4 Picture clue
6 Picture clue
8 Picture clue
10 Purpose of employ (3)
14 Leapt about as a flower part (5)
15 A loam churned up in Texan fight (5)

ACROSS

1a. Negative index of good looks! (3,8)

9a. Terribly (7)

13a. With no hostility (2,5)

18a. Marine fighters (5,6)

DOWN

1d. This is for show-offs! (11)

4d. Old players (11)

6d. Hole enlarging (7)

8d. Money due (7)

PITCHERWITS 3

ACROSS

1 Picture clue
7 Angry, and somehow lanky (5)
8 Picture clue
11 Nick, botching, but not big style (5)
13 Correct omissions in right hand page (5)
14 Picture clue
16 Weight is oddly on cue (5)
18 Picture clue

DOWN

2 Now, how to have... (3)
3 Picture clue
4 Tied around 'process' text (4)
5 Picture clue
6 Picture clue
9 Picture clue
10 Fine picture detail of grand story (4)
12 Phantom, belonging inside grave (4)
15 Venomous one's not, if made like an egg (4)
17 Religious type is a bit of conundrum (3)

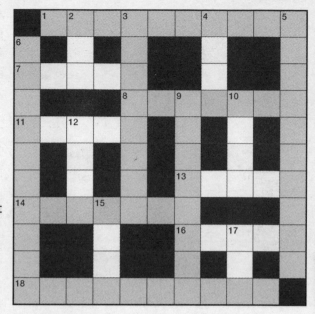

ACROSS

1a. Romantic fellows? (10)

8a. Gentlest (7)

14a. Notice board, with no Edna, is unfeeling (7)

18a. Fly boatman can be showy and colourful (10)

DOWN

3d. Aerial bed-linen? (3,5)

5d. E Asian republic (5,5)

6d. Mansard (6,4)

9d. It's neatly written! (4,4)

ACROSS

1 Picture clue

5 Picture clue

8 Carpentry nowhere near being made into vault (5)

9 Weird talk of where the eagle has landed (5)

10 Embellish radon dispersion (5)

12 Finally, it's goodbye (5)

14 Picture clue

15 Picture clue

DOWN

1 Picture clue

2 Vacuous sound of Mrs Tiggy-winkle at first (5)

3 Bury in between (5)

4 Picture clue

6 Picture clue

7 Picture clue

11 Desert well - with flowers stuck in it? (5)

13 Concept left - to perfection! (5)

ACROSS

1a. Hot work on the mineral! (3,8)

5a. Dramatically small (7)

14a. Vitality (7)

15a. Imperiously, with total skill (11)

DOWN

1d. Government administrators (11)

4d. Belt controller (5,6)

6d. Fraser's her follower (7)

7d. ...and relax (3,4)

PITCHERWITS 3

ACROSS

1. Picture clue
5. Supporting, in conformity (3)
6. ...also in cartoon form (3)
7. Picture clue
10. Peaks upset French, and lost (3)
11. Stretching – like a Sherpa, say? (7)
12. Sort of goblin you could cook on? (3)
13. Picture clue
16. Loafer (bit of a yob, actually) (3)
17. Wise night-flyer in bowler hat (3)
18. Picture clue

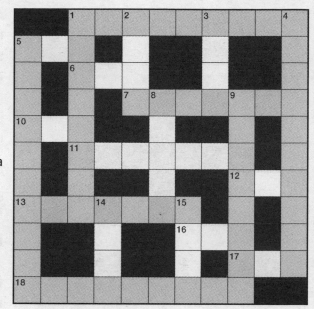

DOWN

1. Picture clue
2. Host is upset by report (4)
3. Augur, drilled out from my abode (4)
4. Picture clue
5. Picture clue
8. Superior crowd – can make you sad? (5)
9. Picture clue
14. Link design to oven (4)
15. Heard you were that blue when alone (4)

ACROSS

1a. Brought together (9)

7a. Airy? (7)

13a. Points of power (7)

18a. For recipes that are a bit thick? (9)

DOWN

1d. Aesthetic is it? Cart overturned more like! (8)

4d. It has value, currently, in USA (6,4)

5d. Next century, sort of (10)

9d. Champion (5,3)

PITCHERWITS 3

ACROSS

1 Picture clue

5 Picture clue

7 Corruptible form of navel studying (5)

8 Remember to finish what's left of the fire... (5)

9 Chances - take them! (5)

11 Award that's said to lever open (5)

12 Picture clue

13 Picture clue

DOWN

1 Picture clue

2 Tag can be all (5)

3 Test a recipe for flavour (5)

4 Picture clue

5 Picture clue

6 Picture clue

10 Ken is made to look like Hank (5)

11 Faye's said to have the stage (5)

ACROSS

1a. Totally out of control (2,1,4,4)

5a. Users - be organised for the Pitcherwits! (7)

12a. Looking at rank? (7)

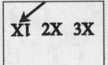

13a. Examination (3,4,4)

DOWN

1d. Without awareness (11)

4d. "We won't give in!" (2,9)

5d. Calls... (5,2)

6d. Die down (7)

PITCHERWITS 3

ACROSS

1 Picture clue
5 Picture clue
9 Think you can find it in the dark? (4)
10 Criminal group of hooligan good-for-nothings (4)
11 Anaesthetic - had at your own pub? (5)
12 Echo-sounding of frost (4)
14 Custom-built, but a bit grave (4)
15 Picture clue
18 Picture clue

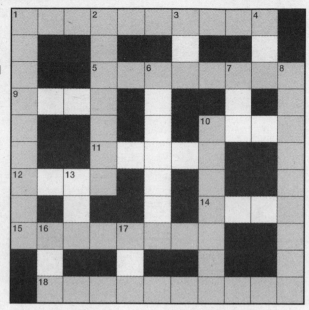

DOWN

1 Picture clue
2 Picture clue
3 Pest is ultimately petulant (3)
4 Spirit - of diesel fuel? (3)
6 Bitterness of the classifier, allegedly (7)
7 Roman eggs all finished? (3)
8 Picture clue
10 Picture clue
13 Coaster in formatted setting (3)
16 States, "It's partly re-usable..." (3)
17 Pelt, say, the evergreen (3)

ACROSS

1a. Can rot (10)

5a. Carries away (5,3)

15a. No tax here! (4-4)

18a. Panic timer? (5,5)

DOWN

1d. Sent and arrived (9)

2d. Use again (7)

8d. Resist actively (5,4)

10d. Muscles - to sit on? (7)

PITCHERWITS 3

ACROSS

1 Picture clue
5 Picture clue
9 False god said to be inactive (4)
10 Clean, having been given a head start (4)
11 She's among clientele names (5)
12 Overhear nothing of merit (4)
13 Against something to earn (4)
14 Picture clue
16 Picture clue

DOWN

1 Picture clue
2 Flash-bulbs, with little weights on the end (3)
3 Rock concert - in a little rower? (3)
4 Picture clue
6 Picture clue
7 Crazy offer's operation to cordon (4,3)
8 Picture clue

14 Obtain fringe to trim (3)
15 Geranium cutting - what an age! (3)

ACROSS

1a. It's a mass of solution (5,6)

5a. Frugal (7)

14a. Warmer... (3,4)

16a. Get 7 (3,3,5)

DOWN

1d. Steel formation place (7,4)

4d. Half-hour comic, eh? (4,7)

6d. This is corny! (7)

8d. Current philosopher? (3,4)

PITCHERWITS 3

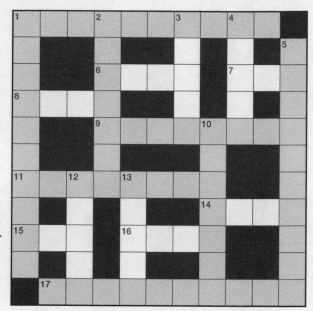

ACROSS

1 Picture clue
6 Flippant start to coin toss (4)
7 Scooter making a bit of a bird noise (3)
8 Break bail in Indonesia (4)
9 Picture clue
11 Picture clue
14 Renovate bit of a star (4)
15 Stern bit of water travel (3)
16 Spotty outbreak of cane... (4)
17 Picture clue

DOWN

1 Picture clue
2 Picture clue
3 Theme of the best in charge (5)
4 Outspoken sort of lyric? (5)
5 Picture clue
10 Picture clue
12 I bail out - as an excuse (5)
13 Look! A piece of little giraffe... (5)

ACROSS

1a. Adorning (10)

9a. Laughed - low? (8)

11a. Accompany (2,6)

17a. Lessens (10)

DOWN

1d. Gives off low vibes (6,4)

2d. Policeman (7)

5d. Body language for hostile, maybe (6,4)

10d. Personal filters (7)

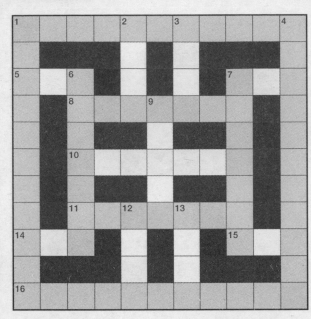

ACROSS

1 Picture clue
5 Cognitive bit of gear... (3)
7 Better yet - bottled whiskey (3)
8 Picture clue
10 A mixture of a mixture of glee, man! (7)
11 Picture clue
14 Look both ways... (3)
15 A bit thick-skinned for snow-travel (3)
16 Picture clue

DOWN

1 Picture clue
2 Hello? A mighty bit of soil (4)
3 Not all brown or white... nor a mixture! (4)
4 Picture clue
6 Picture clue
7 Picture clue
9 Accumulate, claiming to be donkey (5)
12 Connecting point, it's a done deal (4)
13 Fish, with one finale (4)

ACROSS

1a. Given for peace, say (5,6)

8a. Bucharest country (7)

11a. Could get in the way of a good pic! (4,3)

16a. Arrange to impress (5-6)

DOWN

1d. Polite attribute (4,7)

4d. Mallard, say (5,6)

6d. Complain (7)

7d. Wild parties (4-3)

PITCHERWITS 3

ACROSS

1 Picture clue

5 Picture clue

9 Places to coil round (4)

10 Supertax - is less for a cab (4)

11 Religious leader I swam before (5)

12 Tidy section, delineated (4)

14 A hot dish, often sworn (4)

15 Picture clue

18 Picture clue

DOWN

1 Picture clue
2 Picture clue
3 Tree has been modified (3)
4 Pair that's partly deciduous (3)
6 Pokes at strange address (5,2)
7 Pleasing bit of meadow (3)
8 Picture clue
10 Picture clue
13 Single party - such a bother! (3)
16 Steal Roy's partner (3)
17 Roman sun god - not against a parasol (3)

ACROSS

1a. Pulled out (10)

5a. Runny money? (4,4)

15a. Takes to, en route (5,3)

18a. Cook's uniform? (6,4)

DOWN

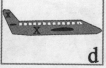
1d. Gave reasons for (9)

2d. Bluest (7)

8d. Spur Lane? (5,4)

10d. Inside information (3-4)

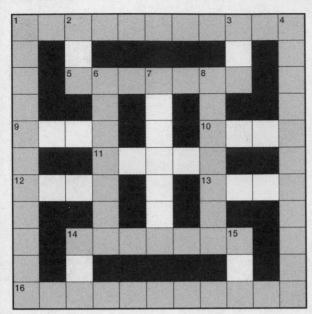

ACROSS

1 Picture clue

5 Picture clue

9 Club for the greens (4)

10 Against prime worker (4)

11 Duskiest - 'tis not for noblemen (5)

12 Gigolos leading with computer-babble? (1,1,1,1)

13 Assume teak to be carved up (4)

14 Picture clue

16 Picture clue

DOWN

1 Picture clue

2 Tear down the epitaph (3)

3 Manage the end of time (3)

4 Picture clue

6 Picture clue

7 Cab work used for film courting? (4,3)

8 Picture clue

14 Flying fisher from Milwaukee (3)

15 Spaniel's very first bath (3)

ACROSS

1a. Bright one! (7,4)

5a. The will to be certain (7)

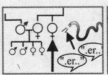

14a. WRENS, as shown in responses (7)

16a. Understand this? (4,2,5)

DOWN

1d. Address collection (7,4)

4d. Thoughtful state (7,4)

6d. What the tears did... (3,4)

8d. He raises his glass – to cook bread (7)

PITCHERWITS 3

ACROSS

1 Picture clue
7 Say Hi! from Hawaii (5)
8 Swimmer totters inwardly (5)
9 Picture clue
11 Picture clue
14 Asian republic seen in diagrammatic form (5)
15 Straighten nuisance - out of boredom (5)
16 Picture clue

DOWN

1 Picture clue
2 Decorate fuss over royal navy (5)
3 Oceanic sort of change? (3)
4 Picture clue
5 Upset duo to do better (5)
6 Picture clue
10 Picture clue
12 Aimed around the papers, say (5)
13 Invalidate, but not as annuals (5)
15 Literature of the age (3)

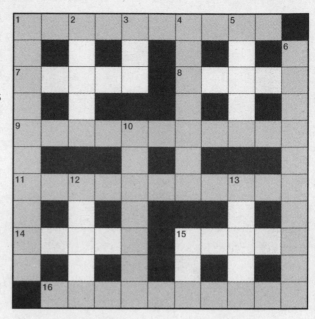

ACROSS

1a. Tries to hurt - a bit! (5,1,4)

9a. Cathedral workers (5,6)

11a. Have words... (11)

16a. Strong rooms? (4,6)

DOWN

1d. Old crooner (4,6)

4d. Market state (7)

6d. Eateries (10)

10d. Search, roughly... (7)

ACROSS

1 Picture clue

5 Picture clue

8 Pre-fix the burial term? (5)

9 Refute that the brute is in trouble (5)

10 Climb over, in place of suspension (5)

12 Cart off bacterium so as to permeate (5)

14 Picture clue

15 Picture clue

DOWN

1 Picture clue

2 No scissors - it's the director's version (5)

3 Pulse under heart

4 Picture clue

6 Picture clue

7 Picture clue

11 Fruit, without the would be pin-up (5)

13 Mad to ban conducting rod (5)

melodeon (5)

ACROSS

1a. Wimbledon comic? (5,6)

5a. Tree (7)

14a. Play, ending... (4,3)

15a. Slippy, ropey thing (7,4)

DOWN

1d. Brassica, sort of (11)

4d. Cause bother (4,3,4)

6d. Gets less wide (7)

7d. Laminate (7)

PITCHERWITS 3

ACROSS

1 Picture clue
5 Initially get your muscles fit in here (3)
6 For each person in front (3)
7 Picture clue
10 Time for a bit of veracity! (3)
11 Arrange for clients to see printing tool (7)
12 Invalid ending, but still top (3)
13 Picture clue
16 Either way, it's useless... (3)
17 Runabout to hold the tea (3)
18 Picture clue

DOWN

1 Picture clue
2 Complain about the fish (4)
3 Looking up to greedy opera star (4)
4 Picture clue
5 Picture clue
8 Main nerve-centre is a tube (5)
9 Picture clue
14 Custom built, in cemetery (4)
15 Need I take on board a cut? (4)

ACROSS

1a. Going beyond (9)

7a. Matador's crony (7)

13a. ...so they don't have to be ordered (2,5)

18a. 40 (not 42) (6,3)

DOWN

1d. Stress, but not strain (8)

4d. Slowed - proportionally (6,4)

5d. Site, sort of (10)

9d. ...with her 'warpaint'? (6,2)

PITCHERWITS 3

ACROSS

1 Picture clue
5 Confused - by a teasmade! (2,3)
7 Tree made of broken panes (5)
9 Picture clue
11 'Donkey' section of assault course (3)
12 Owns, with a simple centre... (3)
13 Picture clue
16 Frequently said about 'X' (5)
17 In central Ibiza - with a reason for absence (5)
18 Picture clue

DOWN

1 Picture clue
2 They're almost in the kingdom (5)
3 Tartan with deep-laid ending (5)
4 Picture clue
6 Picture clue
8 Picture clue
10 Curvy bits of all star cast (3)
14 Dance that can go haywire (5)
15 Game I played for a picture (5)

ACROSS

1a. Gizmo (11)

9a. Roving sort of mad icon (7)

13a. Realistically, a composer? (7)

18a. Sub, but not underwater (11)

DOWN

1d. Protection for the night, say? (5,6)

4d. Characterless (11)

6d. Acne on a solar scale? (7)

8d. Board game (7)

PITCHERWITS 3

ACROSS

1 Picture clue

7 Led on to become ancient (5)

8 Picture clue

11 Funny thing, this dark time... (5)

13 Breakable, but not real, about meat dish (5)

14 Picture clue

16 Praise once was a lot back... (5)

18 Picture clue

DOWN

2 Half afraid to help (3)

3 Picture clue

4 Deadened area of penumbra (4)

5 Picture clue

6 Picture clue

9 Picture clue

10 Concealed - an incomparably beautiful horse (4)

12 Sticky stuff left in is miserable (4)

15 Drove round in excess (4)

17 It's excessive also (3)

ACROSS

1a. Rudeness (3,7)

8a. Outside the perimeter (3-4)

14a. Regret of code double? (7)

18a. Facial look (10)

DOWN

3d. Theseus did for this one! (8)

5d. This'll keep your wheels on! (6,4)

6d. Current value (5,5)

9d. Permanent (3,5)

ACROSS

1 Picture clue

5 Picture clue

8 Paddle it either way here (5)

9 Jewel that turned paler (5)

10 Widen out for the Northumbrian king (5)

12 Little salamanders - intoxication indices? (5)

14 Picture clue

15 Picture clue

DOWN

1 Picture clue

2 Sleepy pal, Big Ears? (5)

3 Oaths taken in border (5)

4 Picture clue

6 Picture clue

7 Picture clue

11 Celtic language of trowel's handle (5)

13 How, I'd think, to give measurement (5)

ACROSS

1a. Clouseau films (4,7)

5a. Particulars (7)

14a. Lid, seen as a flax product (7)

15a. Learnedness - that's worth money? (11)

DOWN

1d. Green space workers (4,7)

4d. Makes for a noisy approach (6,5)

6d. Succoured, say (5,2)

7d. Mini-peg, designed to bear upon (7)

PITCHERWITS 3

ACROSS

1 Picture clue
5 Disparaging of Mother's ruin (3)
6 Pelt lost in blast-furnace (3)
7 Picture clue
10 ...and back to cell molecule (1,1,1)
11 Temperamental artiste has more flavour (7)
12 Coat masked in diplomacy (3)
13 Picture clue
16 One way to be a bit fresh! (3)
17 It's 10 modification as well (3)
18 Picture clue

DOWN

1 Picture clue
2 Water sport - of the net? (4)
3 One gamble to help (4)
4 Picture clue

5 Picture clue
8 Neat ticking off in upper room (5)
9 Picture clue
14 Put money away for rescue (4)

15 Weave wool from bulk nitrogen (4)

ACROSS

1a. Cover (9)

7a. More distant, say Pop? (7)

13a. It's black from head to toe (7)

18a. Nothing to admit... (4,5)

DOWN

1d. Pumps up (8)

4d. Well dug in (10)

5d. Made Moses livid! (6,4)

9d. Safe to be kept out of (5,3)

ACROSS

1 Picture clue

5 Picture clue

7 Joint could be trade (5)

8 Armature goes back and forth (5)

9 Accommodate - in a deceitful sort of way? (3-2)

11 Beau was in a mess (5)

12 Picture clue

13 Picture clue

DOWN

1 Picture clue

2 Bold entrance - a bit ancient (5)

3 Pelt around me? Backbone! (5)

4 Picture clue

5 Picture clue

6 Picture clue

10 Aphorism has not been made the best (5)

11 Kind of preview to snake round? (5)

ACROSS

1a. Not friends of the kitchen gardens! (6,5)

5a. This doesn't augur well... (3,4)

12a. Such foolish innocence... (7)

13a. Apple? It's a big one! (3,4,4)

DOWN

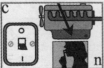

1d. Intake (11)

4d. Sunpower (5,6)

5d. Integral (5-2)

6d. "Phew!" say (3,4)

ACROSS

1 Picture clue
5 Picture clue
9 Fruit - tastes better than it looks? (4)
10 Pure disaster in S American republic (4)
11 It can happen in ad hoc, cursory pieces (5)
12 Bread that Anna made (4)
14 Prima donna - she's right greedy (4)
15 Picture clue
18 Picture clue

DOWN

1 Picture clue
2 Picture clue
3 Spot the Bishop's turf (3)
4 Just me, begorrah! (Well, a bit...) (3)
6 Rick let fly at tiny Flo', allegedly (7)
7 Moderated bit of the poem (3)
8 Picture clue
10 Picture clue
13 Melodic atmosphere? (3)
16 Circle Line, surrounded by anarchy (3)
17 Gremlin's a bit impatient! (3)

ACROSS

1a. William, from Cheshire? (4,2,4)

5a. Hall (not of fame, usually) (8)

15a. A lobe, maybe? (8)

18a. Were they wood-working singers? (10)

DOWN

1d. Fashionable elite (4,9)

2d. Attachment (7)

8d. They are there to climb... (9)

10d. Sensible (7)

PITCHERWITS 3

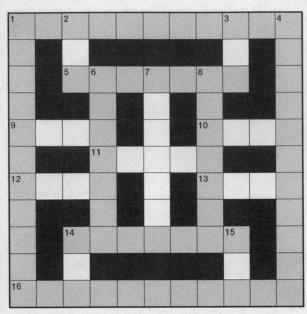

ACROSS

1 Picture clue
5 Picture clue
9 Learning something of merit (4)
10 Pain makes some detached (4)
11 Drilled - with ennui? (5)
12 Vegetable found in bookrack (4)
13 Rustic peasant has appetiser fed to him (4)
14 Picture clue
16 Picture clue

DOWN

1 Picture clue
2 "Stop filming" onset (3)
3 Take in ETA that's miscalculated (3)
4 Picture clue
6 Picture clue
7 Purged a kind of improved hardware (7)
8 Picture clue
14 What Vic. does to his engine? (3)
15 Little adder - either way? (3)

ACROSS

1a. SDAOR, e.g. (11)

5a. Action that's mental (7)

14a. Acknowledgment of payment (7)

16a. Trafalgar, say (5,6)

DOWN

1d. For drinking music? (6,5)

4d. That's real... (5,2,4)

6d. Herbaceous and toxic (7)

8d. Reminding (5-2)

PITCHERWITS 3

ACROSS

1 Picture clue

6 Bottom of the trumpet (4)

7 Transport - with a bit of aftercare (3)

8 ...under - it's Antipodian (4)

9 Picture clue

11 Picture clue

14 Reduction - as of a settee (4)

15 Tree growing in pith helmet (3)

16 It's classy to shop around (4)

17 Picture clue

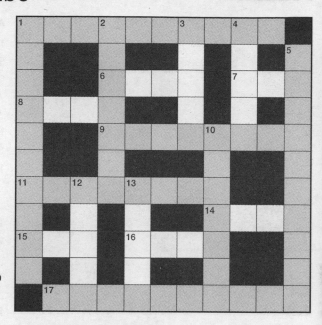

DOWN

1 Picture clue

2 Picture clue

3 Packed out and de-coded (twice) - ruined! (5)

4 Right hand page, said to have spoiled nothing (5)

5 Picture clue

10 Picture clue

12 Bit of a conundrum, ballet-dance... (5)

13 Succesfully resist repeal with a ban (5)

ACROSS

1a. Used for chatty cuisine? (3,7)

9a. Determines (8)

11a. Draughty masonry? (8)

17a. ...the wrong crowd, maybe? (4,2,4)

DOWN

1d. Times of prosperity (6,4)

2d. Yellow vegetable head (7)

5d. Line shade - with an angry cover? (5-5)

10d. Transport provided by Richard Shaw? (7)

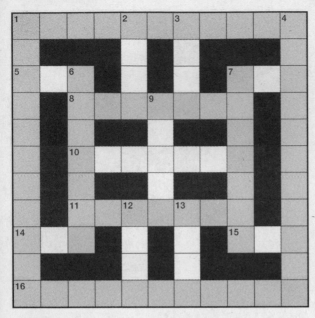

ACROSS

1 Picture clue
5 Beer sales - off the old ship (3)
7 Disapproval - of bookmakers at first (3)
8 Picture clue
10 Last up, a sort of cooking tool... (7)
11 Picture clue
14 Barrel to make good extract (3)
15 Seen in terrible mistake (3)
16 Picture clue

DOWN

1 Picture clue
2 Bit of a list? Time to be creative! (4)
3 Neat sort of magma spout (4)
4 Picture clue

6 Picture clue
7 Picture clue
9 Dish of cooked tripe (5)
12 Cab starts with pins, so they say (4)

13 Block type of dancing (4)

ACROSS

1a. A and D supplier (3,5,3)

8a. Act violently (7)

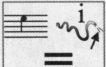

11a. Spots (7)

16a. On and on, it's painful! (7,4)

DOWN

1d. Behind the anchors at sea (5,6)

4d. Became threatening, maybe (6,5)

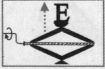

6d. Rubbing out (7)

7d. Four, say (7)

ACROSS

1 Picture clue

5 Picture clue

9 It's that hideous fruit again! (4)

10 What a plane does for a cab (4)

11 Get out gaudiest type of Arabian (5)

12 Lies about little land mass (4)

14 Ill behaved one is a big-headed rodent (4)

15 Picture clue

18 Picture clue

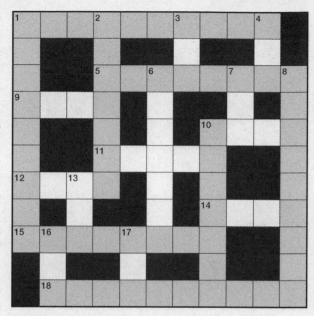

DOWN

1 Picture clue

2 Picture clue

3 She can be seen in the boulevards (3)

4 Wrongdoing is in the ending (3)

6 Bubble bath for Jack? Who's he to talk? (7)

7 An age of literature... (3)

8 Picture clue

10 Picture clue

13 Sleep index - a bit wooden? (3)

16 Indefatigably, it's a bit of a gift (3)

17 Headwear that's from little backstreet (3)

ACROSS

1a. Respites (10)

5a. Next to (8)

15a. It's no yolk for a meringue! (3,5)

18a. Dairy product (10)

DOWN

1d. At last! (5,4)

2d. Tramp, in drunken parties (7)

8d. Thought store? (5,4)

10d. Horizontal batten (3,4)

PITCHERWITS 3

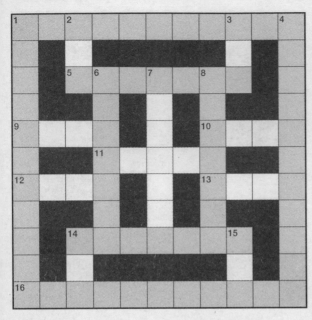

ACROSS

1 Picture clue
5 Picture clue
9 Little biter goes back for a taste (4)
10 Powder in crystal container (4)
11 Speedy way to knock identity, briefly (5)
12 Austria - it's not got atmosphere (4)
13 Anorak loses an arrangement of veg. (4)
14 Picture clue
16 Picture clue

DOWN

1 Picture clue
2 Business section of transport (3)
3 Must pay in the flowerpot (3)
4 Picture clue
6 Picture clue
7 Coin treated, as Pip fled off (7)
8 Picture clue
14 For the short professional? (3)
15 Pull up the tum! (3)

ACROSS

1a. Huh? Anyone at all? (6,5)

5a. Permeate (7)

14a. It's waiting to be sorted! (7)

16a. Improve on (2,3,6)

DOWN

1d. Talking terms (11)

4d. Christmas one that's harmless? (11)

6d. Improved hardware (7)

8d. Parked - personally! (3,4)

ACROSS

1 Picture clue

7 Flat heels trimmed for Turner (5)

8 Salon-type borrowings (5)

9 Picture clue

11 Picture clue

14 Aidan comes back to her (5)

15 Drum has the good French to a turn (5)

16 Picture clue

DOWN

1 Picture clue

2 KwaZulu place of birth (5)

3 Administered a little bit before (3)

4 Picture clue

5 Colour said to be essential for driving (5)

6 Picture clue

10 Picture clue

12 Sound erased, but hiding beneath (5)

13 Extension (off-site) is a gas! (5)

15 Food protector - best tucker's partner (3)

ACROSS

1a. Gateau to liven you up? (6,4)

9a. One with a 'bob or two' (11)

11a. No stress here then! (7,4)

16a. They're flagged up for old pirates (10)

DOWN

1d. Digging for the best? (4,6)

4d. Nutty sounding military rank (7)

6d. Disparaging remarks (10)

10d. Intrusions (7)

PUZZLE 113

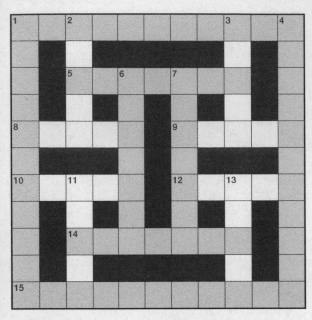

ACROSS

1 Picture clue
5 Picture clue
8 Idly made letterhead into rustic poem (5)
9 Sound of coins being changed (5)
10 Make self-conscious at a party? (5)
12 Dictator's scar removed, leaving same thing! (5)
14 Picture clue
15 Picture clue

DOWN

1 Picture clue
2 With flavour, but not as tyres partly worn (5)
3 Educate in art work (5)
4 Picture clue
6 Picture clue
7 Picture clue
11 Poplar - like the writer (5)
13 Flavour of a test badly set (5)

ACROSS

1a. Hackneyed (3-8)

5a. So cold! (7)

14a. Fruits (7)

15a. They just won't get going! (3-8)

DOWN

1d. Why we're all flawed? (8,3)

4d. Listings (11)

6d. He's a hotel porter in the States (7)

7d. Sabbath (4,3)

PITCHERWITS 3

ACROSS

1 Picture clue
5 Tuneful wind stuff? (3)
6 Terrific, but has mistake in it! (3)
7 Picture clue
10 Such an English tree! (3)
11 Rail against and vie? Nigh impossible! (7)
12 Bird with reduced appetite (3)
13 Picture clue
16 Renovation uncovers eggs (3)
17 No, not the sort of men who creep (3)
18 Picture clue

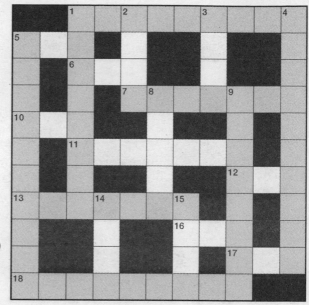

DOWN

1 Picture clue
2 Sinister quality of French old boat (4)
3 Harvest, gone pear-shaped (4)
4 Picture clue
5 Picture clue
8 Representative - bit of a nice guy? (5)
9 Picture clue
14 No-one loses the way this time (4)
15 Oboists a bit taken aback at being 'moderate' (2-2)

ACROSS

1a. Not beneficial to you (3,3,3)

7a. Uganda's biggest (7)

13a. They can be attractive... (7)

18a. Teutonic award (4,5)

DOWN

1d. ...news, sometimes (8)

4d. Mobile stairs? (10)

5d. Dating system - for years and years (4,6)

9d. They can take your butt! (8)

ACROSS

1 Picture clue
5 Mary O'Delaney has her own singing style (5)
7 Beginning to be where film's made? (5)
9 Picture clue
11 Trapped in a style of music (3)
12 Sort of bag in the kitchen (3)
13 Picture clue
16 Drain works reach low point (5)
17 Once, a sort of craft... (5)
18 Picture clue

DOWN

1 Picture clue
2 Many long-johns contain synthetic material (5)
3 Cardamon gradually reduced within (5)

4 Picture clue
6 Picture clue
8 Picture clue
10 Bit of chicken feed for little Kenneth! (3)

14 Throw the runes - a help in hospital (5)
15 Extra large? sounds to be outstanding! (5)

ACROSS

1a. Start of a paragraph (11)

9a. Kingpin stripped down for drinking (4,3)

13a. Finches (7)

18a. Trip devoid of atmosphere (11)

DOWN

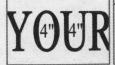

1d. Responsibility's not mine! (2,4,5)

4d. Money earned on the web? (3,8)

6d. It's patchy! (7)

8d. Dawns (5,2)

PITCHERWITS 3

ACROSS

1 Picture clue
7 Revolting type is in there - below! (5)
8 Picture clue
11 Inundated with a cleaning process (5)
13 Additional bit (in next race...) (5)
14 Picture clue
16 Seen around? - turn and follow! (5)
18 Picture clue

DOWN

2 Major Barbara, holding a ball (3)
3 Picture clue
4 Kit for a bike chain? (4)
5 Picture clue
6 Picture clue
9 Picture clue
10 Sent around site for layer-work (4)
12 Opposed to, in the meantime... (4)
15 French town, according to relative (4)
17 Wickedness in advertising (3)

ACROSS

1a. ...with excuses (7,3)

8a. Beginner (7)

14a. Toper (7)

18a. It's closest, viewers! (10)

DOWN

3d. Long cutter (8)

5d. It'll take two pairs... (4-6)

6d. Took the best (7,3)

9d. Another one of you? (5,3)

ACROSS

1 Picture clue

5 Picture clue

8 Greeks said to have tea on the table (5)

9 Tessa returns for a useful attribute (5)

10 Test, about to include a flavour (5)

12 Flower cluster is not from sublime mutation (5)

14 Picture clue

15 Picture clue

13 Tired but in trouble, arithmetically (5)

DOWN

1 Picture clue

2 Trick - from duck! (5)

3 Water hole for flower arrangers? (5)

4 Picture clue

6 Picture clue

7 Picture clue

11 Little boat seen at dusk, if found to be less (5)

ACROSS

1a. In your paintbox (6,5)

5a. Removes explosive possibilities (7)

14a. Positioned (2,5)

15a. Danger second? (6,5)

DOWN

1d. Make you cry? (4,2,5)

4d. Owl habit (5,6)

6d. Incriminate at the photographers? (5-2)

7d. Cooking tool (7)

PITCHERWITS 3

PUZZLE 118

ACROSS

1 Picture clue
5 Talking gift, measured in megabytes (3)
6 Do's set up to be earthy (3)
7 Picture clue
10 Woman of habit? (3)
11 He gives me advice, I bet (7)
12 Horrible female dairy worker (3)
13 Picture clue
16 Eggs said to be six on pitch (3)
17 Vogue piece of advice... (3)
18 Picture clue

DOWN

1 Picture clue
2 Not even probabilities.... (4)
3 Expensive - read about it! (4)
4 Picture clue
5 Picture clue
8 Macaroni, maybe, in the same position as b? (5)
9 Picture clue
14 Two ways in which to hold the number (4)
15 Fake Goya is a technique (4)

ACROSS

1a. There's lots and lots... (9)

7a. Garden plant (7)

13a. Public inspection time (4,3)

18a. Is he appealing? (9)

DOWN

1d. Liqueur (8)

4d. Reverse (2,8)

5d. Joining up, sailor (5,2,3)

9d. Flying machine (8)

ACROSS

1 Picture clue

5 Picture clue

7 Put out former pelmet front (5)

8 Garden dressing is much, in mid-Wales (5)

9 Little boat is skew-whiff. Whew! - it's not (5)

11 Suddenly occur in a 3-D book (3-2)

12 Picture clue

13 Picture clue

DOWN

1 Picture clue

2 Competitor has a viral infection (5)

3 Saying about income tax - without a cent (5)

4 Picture clue

5 Picture clue

6 Picture clue

10 Flan I cooked for the endgame (5)

11 Terrible pain, about to add to fear (5)

ACROSS

1a. Data (11)

5a. Complain bitterly against (7)

12a. Occupation? (7)

13a. Fancy sewing? (11)

DOWN

1d. Make fully aware (7,4)

4d. Irrelevant (3,3,5)

5d. Mark on (7)

6d. Not your full wages (4-3)

PITCHERWITS 3

ACROSS

1 Picture clue
5 Picture clue
9 Across it, you're in America! (4)
10 Lied about being lazy (4)
11 Said to be a miserable old tale-teller (5)
12 Reduced lesson is on/off (4)
14 Fear nothing of merit (4)
15 Picture clue
18 Picture clue

DOWN

1 Picture clue
2 Picture clue
3 Fish eggs laid in aero engines (3)
4 Self-ish bit of cape gooseberry? (3)
6 Apprentice eater in discomfort (7)
7 Ancient type of testament? (3)
8 Picture clue
10 Picture clue
13 Total number of possums (3)
16 Struggle a bit to find Mat (3)
17 Smooth, but a bit like talking bull... (3)

ACROSS

1a. Much to pay (1,4,5)

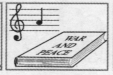
5a. Pocket memo pad (8)

15a. Weaponry (8)

18a. Do a top trip? (2,3,1,4)

DOWN

1d. Voice the only instrument... (1,8)

2d. They fetch, after reports (7)

8d. Maintaining (7,2)

10d. It's very moving... (7)

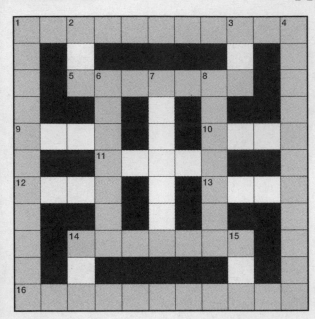

ACROSS

1 Picture clue

5 Picture clue

9 Strange tale of a duck (4)

10 One custom extra? (4)

11 More from complex trading (5)

12 Made a good prophet from a pound (4)

13 Finest axioms surrounding cab (4)

14 Picture clue

16 Picture clue

DOWN

1 Picture clue

2 Advice at the end (3)

3 Said to be eye treatment, literally (3)

4 Picture clue

6 Picture clue

7 Duets to perform for creepy Roman soldiers? (7)

8 Picture clue

14 Beaker, sucker? (3)

15 Wednesday after pancakes? (3)

ACROSS

1a. How pathetic! (5-6)

5a. Object (7)

14a. Spanish island (7)

16a. Correct in law? (5,6)

DOWN

1d. Clown around (4,3,4)

4d. Is faithless? (11)

6d. Give out (7)

8d. A sitcom disaster... of the body (7)

PITCHERWITS 3

ACROSS

1 Picture clue
6 Should end the current moisture (4)
7 Magnificent bit of cold crystal (3)
8 Den of twisted rail (4)
9 Picture clue
11 Picture clue
14 The polish to be embarrassed in, in public? (4)
15 Bit juvenile on pitch? That's nothing! (3)
16 Oral exam in Old Vauxhall (4)
17 Picture clue

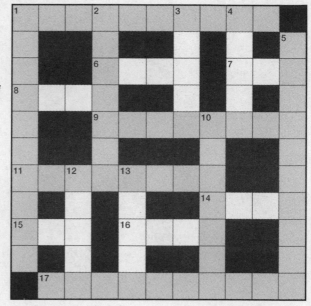

DOWN

1 Picture clue
2 Picture clue
3 Those pianos are brown in parts (5)
4 Middle of the road Liberal has covering reason (5)
5 Picture clue
10 Picture clue
12 Snow home built with i-adhesive? (5)
13 Stomach talk of the sea service (5)

ACROSS

1a. Present time for Pop? (7,3)

9a. Scratchy! (8)

11a. See you soon, Ma'mselle! (1,7)

17a. "Let's...." (2,3,1,4)

DOWN

1d. Experiences dizziness? (5,5)

2d. Supply water (7)

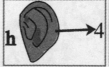

5d. Up to now... (10)

10d. ...and enjoy! (3,4)

ACROSS

1 Picture clue
5 Top type is a computer (3)
7 ...cry, therefore, at bad start (3)
8 Picture clue
10 Daytime performance - a format in eerie parts (7)
11 Picture clue
14 Cereal stuck at back of throat (3)
15 Snow travel, in back of dik-diks (3)
16 Picture clue

DOWN

1 Picture clue
2 Slaking ink off from the waste (4)
3 Double act is a dead index (4)
4 Picture clue
6 Picture clue
7 Picture clue
9 Rule the weather, allegedly (5)
12 'Clothes' with thermal ratings (4)
13 Bit of the list is a mite confused (4)

ACROSS

1a. Squashed (7,4)

8a. Clique (2-5)

11a. Gross (3,4)

16a. Briefly it's the latest (4,7)

DOWN

1d. Lowering (7,4)

4d. High clan? (5,6)

6d. Colouring (7)

7d. Orbs (7)

PITCHERWITS 3

ACROSS

1 Picture clue
5 Picture clue
9 Yellowhammers can shout a bit! (4)
10 Yokel, picking out seaweed (4)
11 Tame leeches in a bit of a scrimmage (5)
12 Part to the left - it's a snare! (4)
14 Little dog coming from... a chrysalis! (4)
15 Picture clue
18 Picture clue

DOWN

1 Picture clue
2 Picture clue
3 Label's a great game of chase (3)
4 A hankering for currency (3)
6 Unfailing, if not somehow an explosive hammer (4,3)
7 Obliged to pay - sound surprised? (3)
8 Picture clue
10 Picture clue
13 Back on board in the rafters (3)
16 To a fault, a bit of a slob (3)
17 Crystal, in basic English... (3)

ACROSS

1a. Utterly (10)

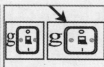

5a. Absent ages ago (4,4)

15a. ...for instant connections? (8)

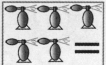

18a. How we perceive things (4,6)

DOWN

1d. Not a homely fixture (4,5)

2d. Kerosene user (3,4)

8d. Big flower (9)

10d. Maintains (5,2)

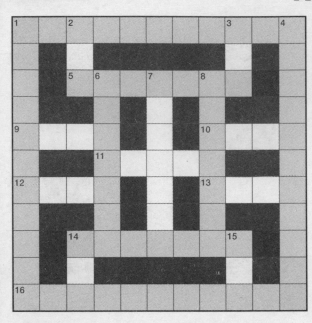

ACROSS

1 Picture clue
5 Picture clue
9 "Fool!" they said, "work in wool" (4)
10 Lad said to decline (4)
11 Spoil the force - and regretting it! (5)
12 Living in a boathouse, you oldie? (4)
13 Flower seen in eye-piece (4)
14 Picture clue
16 Picture clue

DOWN

1 Picture clue
2 Rug said to be rather dull (3)
3 Compete in the 'heavies' League (3)
4 Picture clue
6 Picture clue
7 Abram, I'm about to knock out a tune with it... (7)
8 Picture clue
14 Engine act - bit of an abbreviation (3)
15 Basking in snow travel (3)

ACROSS

1a. Desert ship's captain (5,6)

5a. Little flyers! (7)

14a. Sells a realist out (7)

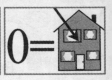

16a. Ain't it just! (4,2,5)

DOWN

1d. Spherical part of match (7,4)

4d. Old UK colony (5,6)

6d. Burst in (7)

8d. She's a herder (7)

PITCHERWITS 3

ACROSS

1 Picture clue
7 Ditch - it's a bird at the end of the day (5)
8 Imp, or substitute, has principal part (5)
9 Picture clue
11 Picture clue
14 She can hoard - very badly (5)
15 Upset, near a stadium (5)
16 Picture clue

DOWN

1 Picture clue
2 Material used in many longboats (5)
3 What hens do without taking orders? (3)
4 Picture clue
5 Window type seen in Loire architecture (5)
6 Picture clue
10 Picture clue
12 It's a gas, with no defined region (5)
13 Scandinavian root veg.? (5)
15 Fire remains a bit squashed... (3)

ACROSS

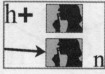
1a. Rub it in, why don't you? (4,6)

9a. Very passionately (11)

11a. Tradition busters (11)

16a. Shuttle protection (4,6)

DOWN

1d. Altitude travellers (4-6)

4d. Optical illusion that's current (7)

6d. Lindisfarne, say... (4,6)

10d. 71 mph. (3,4)

ACROSS

1 Picture clue
5 Picture clue
8 Backlog researched, found to contain monsters (5)
9 Equivalent queen lost out, but somehow critical (5)
10 Oaf is confused in Bulgaria (5)
12 Call a man about a little woolly camel... (5)
14 Picture clue
15 Picture clue

DOWN

1 Picture clue
2 Total, say (5)
3 Should be in thoughtful environment (5)
4 Picture clue
6 Picture clue
7 Picture clue
11 Thrown fag-end on to breathing tackle (5)
13 Review of first audition (5)

ACROSS

1a. Cheque stub (11)

5a. Needlework (7)

14a. Put through 90 deg. (7)

15a. Joint (3,2,6)

DOWN

1d. Metal (6,5)

4d. Barrister-speak (5,6)

6d. Surplus (2,5)

7d. Sufferer (7)

PITCHERWITS 3

ACROSS

1 Picture clue
5 Back to partner (3)
6 Finnegan's pub (3)
7 Picture clue
10 Easter gift? - bit of a beggar! (3)
11 Plum gives pitbull a certain centre (7)
12 Give nickname to step music (3)
13 Picture clue
16 Roman eggs all done? (3)
17 Percentage to be snipped? (3)
18 Picture clue

DOWN

1 Picture clue
2 Yearnings - current in Japan? (4)
3 Put on wording, but dig out (4)
4 Picture clue
5 Picture clue
8 Tonal variation reveals claw (5)
9 Picture clue
14 An ocular sort of flower? (4)
15 Picasso, dancing round a tonic (4)

ACROSS

1a. 5/11 feller (3,6)

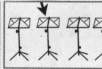

7a. Get ready to fight (5,2)

13a. DNA is in modified form for Delhi folk (7)

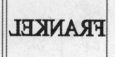

18a. Transportation method (9)

DOWN

1d. Deteriorating (5,3)

4d. Not first rate (6,4)

5d. Extreme excitement (5,5)

9d. What the annuals did (4,4)

ACROSS

1 Picture clue
5 Abbreviations, etc, shortened at the start (5)
7 Overkills - sell out of Russian city (5)
9 Picture clue
11 Port, but not for drinking in Brazil (3)
12 Good man from Magdalene (3)
13 Picture clue
16 Brief - but alcoholic? (5)
17 Lessen nuisance value (out of boredom) (5)
18 Picture clue

DOWN

1 Picture clue
2 Theme of a bon mot, if a little short (5)
3 Sheikhs he deserted for religious types (5)
4 Picture clue
6 Picture clue
8 Picture clue
10 Coups d'etat can provide highs (3)
14 Daft behaviour of cat in trouble (5)
15 Back at sea it's very forbidding (5)

ACROSS

1a. Alloy (6,5)

9a. No - like rubbish? (7)

13a. Frame to roll with (7)

18a. No-harm guarantee (4,7)

DOWN

1d. Joints - not your own! (5,6)

4d. Plant (4-2-1-4)

6d. Windstorm (7)

8d. Turns up (5,2)

PITCHERWITS 3

ACROSS

1 Picture clue
7 I have less trouble with offshore lands (5)
8 Picture clue
11 A libido, beginning life as an excuse (5)
13 Telex trade sections have more... (5)
14 Picture clue
16 Inanimate interchange (5)
18 Picture clue

DOWN

2 Boiled a bit - for a painting! (3)
3 Picture clue
4 Wading bird's alibi soon scaled down (4)
5 Picture clue
6 Picture clue
9 Picture clue
10 Stretched tight - allegedly in school (4)
12 Concept - from a side angle (4)
15 Reverse sound of middle bits (4)
17 Create half to take in (3)

ACROSS

1a. Text amount (6,4)

8a. ...teacake? (7)

14a. Sentence bits (7)

18a. Capital qualities (10)

DOWN

3d. ...and leave (2,6)

5d. Racing advantages (4,6)

6d. Play end (5,5)

9d. Eee by gum, what's sticking? (8)

ACROSS

1 Picture clue

5 Picture clue

8 Houselights - concealing flier (5)

9 Welcome in, pedigree Terrier! (5)

10 Desire at year-end is hearty (5)

12 Hit list is not made up of soil states (5)

14 Picture clue

15 Picture clue

DOWN

1 Picture clue

2 Heads of hair - means turning! (5)

3 Follow on, wearing green suede... (5)

4 Picture clue

6 Picture clue

7 Picture clue

11 Nag could be wise coming to a bad end (5)

13 Behold - donkey jumps into rope (5)

ACROSS

1a. You stay right there! (4,7)

5a. Snacks (7)

14a. Fencing feature (7)

15a. Boxed in (7,2,2)

DOWN

1d. Gas transporter (11)

4d. One long motor! (7,4)

6d. Bad company state (5,2)

7d. Beneficiary (7)

PITCHERWITS 3

ACROSS

1 Picture clue
5 In W India, said to be a goer! (3)
6 Crystals in magnificent surroundings (3)
7 Picture clue
10 Put on back to front, as a gesture (3)
11 Running away with damaged GPO line (7)
12 Ran round, like ribonucleic acid (3)
13 Picture clue
16 Answer's not in here - stumped? (3)
17 Frozen in part of the policy (3)
18 Picture clue

DOWN

1 Picture clue
2 Saw, then curtseyed, at last! (4)
3 Try out at a late stage (4)
4 Picture clue
5 Picture clue
8 Time's in bits of peel to throw out (5)
9 Picture clue
14 Said about a platform... (4)
15 Pool set up in rope pattern (4)

ACROSS

1a. Swim, say, how you want (9)

7a. It's toothy! (7)

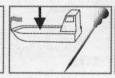
13a. Bag, but not catch (7)

18a. ...with a penknife? (5,4)

DOWN

1d. Decent swap (4,4)

4d. What you think will happen (10)

5d. Like a bargain? (5,5)

9d. Cheesy! (Sorry) (2,6)

PITCHERWITS 3

ACROSS

1 Picture clue

5 Picture clue

7 Deduce ref is back in front (5)

8 I long to mix up 'language' (5)

9 Snitch on the turf (5)

11 Saluki, roving in Russian city (5)

12 Picture clue

13 Picture clue

DOWN

1 Picture clue

2 Forfeit it without making a bid (5)

3 Lied about a perfect state (5)

4 Picture clue

5 Picture clue

6 Picture clue

10 Mates hurt with hot vapour (5)

11 How donkey expresses excitement? (5)

ACROSS

1a. Suggestion (11)

5a. Wrong! (3-4)

12a. Design clients are about.... (7)

13a. Big tops' MC's (11)

DOWN

1d. ...onto the hard shoulder? (7,4)

4d. Bigot's beliefs (6,5)

5d. ...when you don't give your best (3,4)

6d. Spindle (7)

PITCHERWITS 3

ACROSS

1 Picture clue
5 Picture clue
9 Shot wildly? Rubbish! (4)
10 Group of countries in drab locality (4)
11 Crazy tax-payer to pay out more (5)
12 Fibbed about being sort of idle (4)
14 Live Oak (not in little avenue) carries some weight (4)
15 Picture clue
18 Picture clue

DOWN

1 Picture clue
2 Picture clue
3 Agony aunt, from bygone days (3)
4 Alpine travel in one's kid gloves (3)
6 Into this teaching, it would be a hunch (7)
7 Hole maker sounds total (3)
8 Picture clue
10 Picture clue
13 Appendix out is the goal... (3)
16 Got a bit of a piece for a label... (3)
17 Nothing from Manila... (3)

ACROSS

1a. Really high fliers! (10)

5a. So no £200 then? (2,2,4)

15a. Eating (2,6)

18a. Reduce to essential (4,4,2)

DOWN

1d. Not a weight - oz (9)

2d. Corrected (7)

8d. Fixes upon (5,4)

10d. Far from drama (4,3)

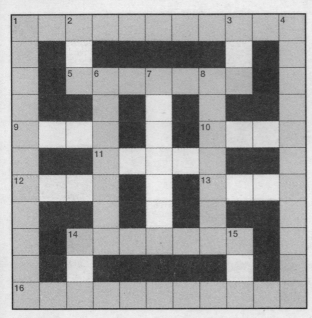

ACROSS

1 Picture clue

5 Picture clue

9 Paper material? Latest! (4)

10 Craziest site, gone from odd Russian ruler (4)

11 Acid, written in biro, roughly (5)

12 Trundle Ltd, out of alphabet character (4)

13 Wean all over again (4)

14 Picture clue

16 Picture clue

DOWN

1 Picture clue

2 Ingest and sweat it out (3)

3 I perceive, I say, that it's freezing (3)

4 Picture clue

6 Picture clue

7 Turns it round for legal responsibility (2,5)

8 Picture clue

14 Sick of leaving the village (3)

15 Released from the meadow (3)

ACROSS

1a. Medicine - for tots (11)

5a. Careful (7)

14a. Primary (7)

16a. Drawing away (7,4)

DOWN

1d. Business concern (11)

4d. Flying hunter (11)

6d. 'Once-was' guy (3-4)

8d. Composition (7)

PITCHERWITS 3

ACROSS

1 Picture clue
6 Reminder of some moment! (4)
7 Pre-bread said to be deer (3)
8 Neat axiom to hide cab (4)
9 Picture clue
11 Picture clue
14 Rosebuds bore out the froth (4)
15 Badger, the old horse... (3)
16 What's said twice with a twist (4)
17 Picture clue

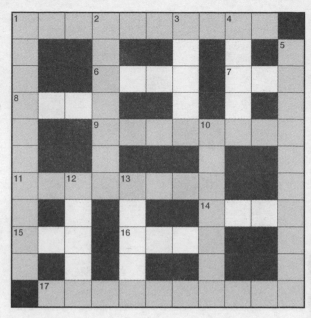

DOWN

1 Picture clue
2 Picture clue
3 Mock - but eat locally (5)
4 Shuddering to contain dairy food source (5)
5 Picture clue
10 Picture clue
12 Portend, but said to be boring (5)
13 The next rack has more... (5)

ACROSS

1a. Primary edition (5,5)

9a. Invitations - from HMRC! (3,5)

11a. Tranquil (8)

17a. What your signal's doing? (8,2)

DOWN

1d. Scruffs' action (3-7)

2d. Coming from Shem, son of Noah (7)

5d. Government restriction (10)

10d. Protection (7)

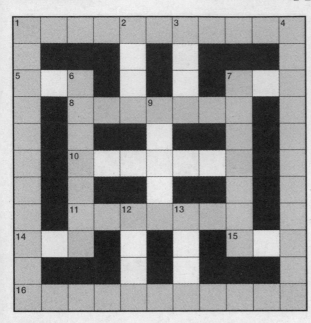

ACROSS

1 Picture clue
5 Formerly looked back... (3)
7 Geller - somewhat furious (3)
8 Picture clue
10 In situ, a kind of African republic (7)
11 Picture clue
14 Policy is ultimately frozen (3)
15 Friskier bit of Alpine travel (3)
16 Picture clue

DOWN

1 Picture clue
2 The thread of the story (4)
3 Architectural bit of foot? (4)
4 Picture clue
6 Picture clue
7 Picture clue
9 Glossy and shy in turn (5)
12 Alter egos stare out in little bricks (4)
13 A sign of male absence (4)

ACROSS

1a. For cheap shopping (5,6)

8a. Family connections (7)

11a. God, would you believe? (4,3)

16a. Racy place! (7,4)

DOWN

1d. From engines to tyres (11)

4d. Create a fuss (5,1,5)

6d. Bare bony? (7)

7d. Keeping you informed... (7)

PITCHERWITS 3

ACROSS

1 Picture clue
5 Picture clue
9 Eleven - finally it's not odd! (4)
10 Tube taken to hold second Greek (4)
11 Stroll by the side of Windermere (5)
12 GM body for George, footballer (4)
14 Earplug - listening in to a bit of fruit (4)
15 Picture clue
18 Picture clue

DOWN

1 Picture clue
2 Picture clue
3 Art form on the roads (3)
4 Individual - at other end of telephone (3)
6 Cook part of a bipolar recipe (7)
7 I've come to compete... (3)
8 Picture clue
10 Picture clue
13 Whoever's doing this Pitcherwits puzzle... (3)
16 Relieve from pride (3)
17 Grab a paltry piece of bread roll (3)

ACROSS

1a. Ready for the off! (3,3,2,2)

5a. Often goes with new... (8)

15a. Falls apart (8)

18a. Glum (10)

DOWN

1d. With no free oxygen (9)

2d. Batter's protection (7)

8d. Bang on! (4,5)

10d. Puzzled... (7)

PITCHERWITS 3

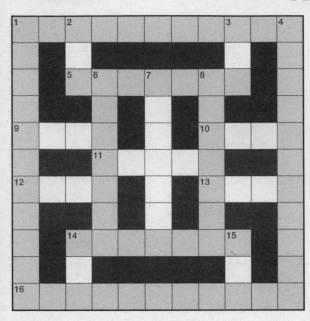

ACROSS

1 Picture clue
5 Picture clue
9 Keen on Toni (sort of) (4)
10 Ripping sound - good for container weight (4)
11 Relative in EEC plan (5)
12 Smaller Paellas for Fitzgerald (4)
13 Well ventilated bit of dairy milk (4)
14 Picture clue
16 Picture clue

DOWN

1 Picture clue
2 Take in half a breath (3)
3 Record of a sound sleep? (3)
4 Picture clue
6 Picture clue
7 Needleworker rowed out to make a pad (7)
8 Picture clue
14 One can be thrown from expediency (3)
15 Fixed part of assets (3)

ACROSS

1a. Deflated (11)

5a. Mattress covering (7)

14a. Pays (7)

16a. Club (not to bash with!) (5,6)

DOWN

1d. European, say (11)

4d. She looks after tots (11)

6d. Was this a pressing era? (4,3)

8d. Difficult one! (3,4)

PITCHERWITS 3

ACROSS

1 Picture clue

7 Only Newton could be material (5)

8 Cry off archway's design being flooded (5)

9 Picture clue

11 Picture clue

14 Training that's boring? (5)

15 An awful pain to ring a musical instrument! (5)

16 Picture clue

DOWN

1 Picture clue
2 Antiquity, in derelict state (5)
3 Layer of Athens (3)
4 Picture clue
5 Mornings that once were tests? (5)
6 Picture clue
10 Picture clue
12 Chain wound round big country (5)
13 Took a piece out of African creature (5)
15 Bit of an opening for a writer (3)

ACROSS

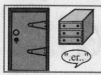
1a. Dorset's London hotel? (10)

9a. Places for better people? (11)

11a. Just not bishops... (11)

16a. Welwyn (6,4)

DOWN

1d. Organ granters (5,5)

4d. A bit bony! (7)

6d. Shudder-maker (5,5)

10d. Processed the egg... (7)

PUZZLE 141

PITCHERWITS 3

ACROSS

1 Picture clue
5 Picture clue
8 Many a strange old Guatemalan, say (5)
9 Searched ads out madly for good spirit (5)
10 Early confusion of stratum (5)
12 MBA as version of Brazilian dance (5)
14 Picture clue
15 Picture clue

DOWN

1 Picture clue
2 No word of a lie, trustily, it's not (5)
3 Spooky sound of a nest (5)
4 Picture clue
6 Picture clue
7 Picture clue
11 Indoor plant? Sounds disgusting at first! (5)
13 How soldiers can dress, civilly (5)

ACROSS

1a. ...by sounding familiar (5,3,3)

5a. Reaching usual level (2,2,3)

14a. Cancel (4,3)

15a. Can't get in... (2,9)

DOWN

1d. Fresh chunk of money? (4,7)

4d. It kicked off the Protestants! (11)

6d. Botanical hanger-on (7)

7d. Spanish dauber (7)

PITCHERWITS 3

ACROSS

1 Picture clue
5 'Tango Alpha' - short for 'Indian province' (3)
6 Pull two - in error (3)
7 Picture clue
10 French-born, in engineering (3)
11 Re-sign - all beer to be brewed (7)
12 It is a groove, in truth (3)
13 Picture clue
16 Make music inside the bird (3)
17 Pop's paper? (1,1,1)
18 Picture clue

DOWN

1 Picture clue
2 Swapping spin-off makes one stare (4)
3 Paint in red/auburn (4)
4 Picture clue
5 Picture clue
8 Employment of sausage (in the end!) (5)
9 Picture clue
14 Novello - firstly a bit of a carnivore (4)
15 Laser action cuts down blood fluids (4)

ACROSS

1a. 'Snuffed it' (6,3)

7a. Return (3,4)

13a. Old courts (7)

18a. Previously mentioned (9)

DOWN

1d. Motifs (8)

4d. Paper strip (6,4)

5d. Chinese bear (5,5)

9d. In every way (3-5)

ACROSS

1 Picture clue
5 Ghanaian city in cardiac crash (5)
7 Keen to agree (sort of) (5)
9 Picture clue
11 Cruelly use her (3)
12 Roman Sun-god - in solution (3)
13 Picture clue
16 Relieved, as a seed "G.M.'d " (5)
17 He'd so be confused if rinsed down (5)
18 Picture clue

DOWN

1 Picture clue
2 Once more, Gina has a design (5)
3 Musical - result of less cooperation (5)
4 Picture clue
6 Picture clue
8 Picture clue
10 Can hold ice cream, but upwards (3)
14 Centre of bad end in fog (5)
15 Some thick-skinned moral! (5)

ACROSS

1a. Coolant lid (8,3)

9a. Answers in a right state! (7)

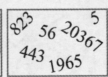

13a. Digital good book 4? (7)

18a. HOORAY! (6,5)

DOWN

1d. ...just from a script (4,1,6)

4d. Corbyn, say... (5,6)

6d. Glues - stonily? (7)

8d. Visionaries?(!) (7)

PITCHERWITS 3

ACROSS

1 Picture clue
7 Flag given to hothead for whiskey (5)
8 Picture clue
11 Engine for team leader (in backroom) (5)
13 Army unit said to have apple pips (5)
14 Picture clue
16 Reddish-brown ape is confused (5)
18 Picture clue

DOWN

2 A bit amateurish, Mr Geller! (3)
3 Picture clue
4 Beige cure, sort of (4)
5 Picture clue
6 Picture clue
9 Picture clue
10 Cross jungle talk? (4)
12 Taste - in a tight angle (4)
15 Stumped when it's on pitch? (4)
17 For every upcoming salesman... (3)

ACROSS

1a. You or me... (5,5)

8a. Made certain (7)

14a. Registration doc. (3,4)

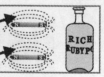

18a. Game of turf? (5,5)

DOWN

3d. Maintain connection (6,2)

5d. For sitting out (6,4)

6d. Well held tenet (4,6)

9d. Makes sense... (6,2)

PITCHERWITS 3

ACROSS

1 Picture clue

5 Picture clue

8 Peak is low when fallen (5)

9 Democrat has no ETA on disc (2-3)

10 Release Aunties' middle! (5)

12 Earl's crazy light beam (5)

14 Picture clue

15 Picture clue

13 Religious leader I swam into trouble with (5)

DOWN

1 Picture clue

2 Rupee's change for strained food (5)

3 Circle in main nervous system (5)

4 Picture clue

6 Picture clue

7 Picture clue

11 Badly taint clashing type (5)

ACROSS

1a. Bringing in... (11)

5a. Salt in the wound? (3,2,2)

14a. African republic (7)

15a. ...as the "Won't see-ers" (4,2,5)

DOWN

1d. Like a hermit (2,9)

4d. Adman's claim! (3,8)

6d. Little heron (7)

7d. Feather effect (7)

PITCHERWITS 3

ACROSS

1 Picture clue
5 Feeble - at half the money (3)
6 Again, it's an afterthought (3)
7 Picture clue
10 Ocean said to be in bishop's turf (3)
11 Caring for the leaning (7)
12 Road glue? It's an art form! (3)
13 Picture clue
16 Bit of sorbet to go with the sceptre (3)
17 Inalienable? A bit of a fib! (3)
18 Picture clue

DOWN

1 Picture clue
2 Fuel, with quiet intake (4)
3 Profound part of Dundee parade (4)
4 Picture clue
5 Picture clue
8 Green donations - from a side view (3-2)
9 Picture clue
14 Animal said to cost a lot (4)
15 The only sound a spirit makes? (4)

ACROSS

1a. About... (9)

7a. Races (not round madly) (7)

13a. Infuriates (7)

18a. Rate too high (9)

DOWN

1d. Said again (8)

4d. Work for author (5,5)

5d. R 'n' B man (4,6)

9d. Old Maths furniture? (3,5)

PITCHERWITS 3

ACROSS

1 Picture clue
5 Picture clue
7 Permanently mark fallen saint (5)
8 Hen-type stratum (5)
9 Clumsy change-over gone green - what chaos! (5)
11 Elbow disjointed from intestine (5)
12 Picture clue
13 Picture clue

DOWN

1 Picture clue
2 Frequently derived from decimal (5)
3 Ghost town in North Humberside? (5)
4 Picture clue
5 Picture clue
6 Picture clue
10 Desert ship arrived, then left (5)
11 Committee that's a game sort? (5)

ACROSS

1a. Butter group (4,2,5)

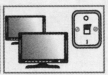

5a. Starts to move (4,3)

12a. Succinct version (7)

13a. He's a pain in the... neck! (7,4)

DOWN

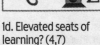

1d. Elevated seats of learning? (4,7)

4d. Don't need anyone! (4-7)

5d. Winter warmers (7)

6d. Hair type? (3-4)

PITCHERWITS 3

ACROSS

1 Picture clue
5 Picture clue
9 It's just as well, in the final song (4)
10 Slope has right current behind it (4)
11 Puree dish with Indian currency (5)
12 Throw in vessel's direction (4)
14 Crazy - for spanners? (4)
15 Picture clue
18 Picture clue

DOWN

1 Picture clue
2 Picture clue
3 Fire remains half-washed (3)
4 Drain made out of pebbles (3)
6 Oil trip round Libyan city (7)
7 Disapproval of eggs in Rome (3)
8 Picture clue
10 Picture clue
13 Lush - up to a point (3)
16 Staid, with no way to help (3)
17 On Beaufort scale, it's out-of-this-world crafty! (3)

ACROSS

1a. Roast pork add-on (5,5)

5a. After-soak wear? (8)

15a. For feline professionals? (8)

18a. Give independence (10)

DOWN

1d. Southern (9)

2d. Slogs away at... (7)

8d. Oh dear dear! (9)

10d. Pulls back excesses (5,2)

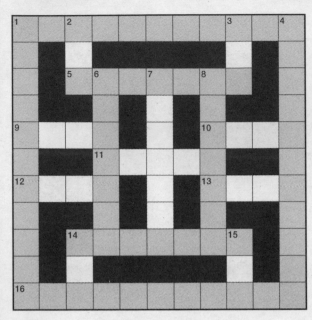

ACROSS

1 Picture clue
5 Picture clue
9 Grown-ups, spurred off by the dress (4)
10 Cow-speak - should end after temper! (4)
11 The lady is a one - footloose and fancy-free? (5)
12 Aeneas left her - because she achieved nothing? (4)
13 Shock! I lost a bit of weight! (4)
14 Picture clue
16 Picture clue

DOWN

1 Picture clue
2 Donkey is like a stop-start (3)
3 Cambridgeshire city to rely on, at last (3)
4 Picture clue
6 Picture clue
7 Teacupful, not first or last, could be a footie tussle (4,3)
8 Picture clue
14 Light touch to control flow from below (3)
15 Age of geranium cutting (3)

ACROSS

1a. Thumping good nail-pullers! (4,7)

5a. Rough cider (7)

14a. On paper, it could be gas.. (7)

16a. Political entity (6-5)

DOWN

1d. Went from 5th to 4th... (7,4)

4d. Green meal stage? (5,6)

6d. Landline (with number) (7)

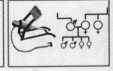

8d. Cinderella pre-transport (7)

PITCHERWITS 3

ACROSS

1 Picture clue
6 Ain't bad for opposing... (4)
7 Medusa's final states (3)
8 Den has lost a bit of flair (4)
9 Picture clue
11 Picture clue
14 Halibut, bit off and shaped as a hoop (4)
15 Magic number the dressmaker uses? (3)
16 Become weary from semi-retirement (4)
17 Picture clue

DOWN

1 Picture clue
2 Picture clue
3 Living in a veil, sort of (5)
4 Quiet chunk is well-rounded (5)
5 Picture clue
10 Picture clue
12 Oxygen, I imagine, to be partially necessary for jinns (5)
13 Upset duo to do better (5)

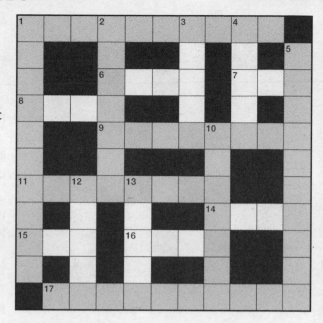

ACROSS

1a. Showy lighters? (5,5)

9a. Chance across (4,4)

11a. ...for a lot of pork (3,5)

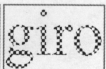

17a. Paper cash support (4,6)

DOWN

1d. So optimistic! (4,2,4)

2d. Not so common (7)

5d. Slow cookers? (5-5)

10d. ...with the best of 'em (2,5)

PITCHERWITS 3

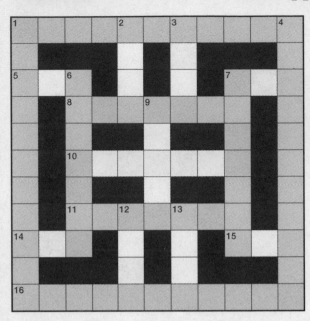

ACROSS

1 Picture clue
5 Furrow has a bad start for champagne (3)
7 Tush! - hidden in airfield (3)
8 Picture clue
10 What's learned from SOS lens (7)
11 Picture clue
14 Big pot for tax? (3)
15 Handy extra bit of colouring (3)
16 Picture clue

DOWN

1 Picture clue
2 Bread, not bone, idle (4)
3 Opposing form of Praying Mantis (4)
4 Picture clue
6 Picture clue
7 Picture clue
9 A loss-adjustment for ropey cowboy gear (5)
12 Swerve, ever changing (4)
13 Novello - somewhat omnivorous (4)

ACROSS

1a. Has an illicit peck? (6,1,4)

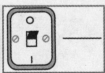

8a. Internetted? No! (7)

11a. Bill (not William) (7)

16a. Shakespeare, e.g. (8,3)

DOWN

1d. Probably above basement (6,5)

4d. From one end to t'other (4,2,5)

6d. Mechanic's holdall (7)

7d. Had a banquet (7)

PITCHERWITS 3

ACROSS

1 Picture clue
5 Picture clue
9 Boat has a bit of a curse (4)
10 Wet type is very slow flow (4)
11 Plié gently in feudal allegiance (5)
12 Bute is taken to be underground (4)
14 Front man for Stravinsky (4)
15 Picture clue
18 Picture clue

DOWN

1 Picture clue
2 Picture clue
3 Curvy bit of parcel (3)
4 Dispose of torrid finale (3)
6 Laramie - turns out it's a Spanish city (7)
7 Neither is it said to chew (3)
8 Picture clue
10 Picture clue
13 Ban legal types (3)
16 Tree has been modified (3)
17 Much rescued by Abraham... (3)

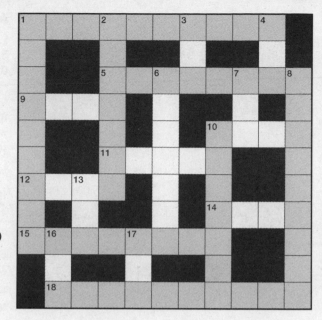

ACROSS

1a. Dispute settler (10)

5a. Tree boa (8)

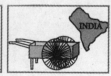

15a. Such a romantic! (8)

18a. ...give you blotches (4,6)

DOWN

1d. Very gymnastic (9)

2d. ...or a jam? (2,1,4)

8d. They're not so penetrating... (5,4)

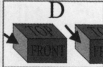

10d. Settles (7)

PITCHERWITS 3

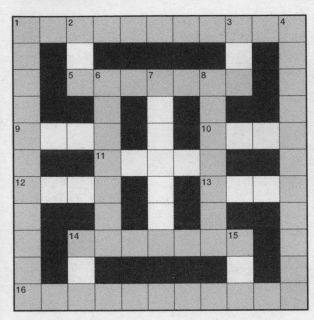

ACROSS

1 Picture clue
5 Picture clue
9 Sort of word for a sort of shark? (4)
10 Rip rate in pieces (4)
11 Panic actions conceal prickly plants (5)
12 'Garbage in - garbage out' - on keyboards (4)
13 Fare badly with angst (4)
14 Picture clue
16 Picture clue

DOWN

1 Picture clue
2 Administration has low type (3)
3 At last - daddy-long-legs as examples (1.1.1)
4 Picture clue
6 Picture clue
7 Get the news - by walking faster? (5,2)
8 Picture clue
14 ...also said to be a duo (3)
15 It's kind of wrapped in silks (3)

ACROSS

1a. 2 words in a bag? (11)

5a. Triple muscles? (7)

14a. Libyan city (7)

16a. Where they sell cows? (5,6)

DOWN

1d. St Peter's entrance? (6,5)

4d. PC to tell you you are, maybe (5,6)

6d. Bitterness (7)

8d. Pathetic (7)

PITCHERWITS 3

ACROSS

1 Picture clue
7 Sunlight said to lift (5)
8 A cub's poor design of breathing tackle (5)
9 Picture clue
11 Picture clue
14 Garden nuisance - can give boredom (5)
15 Squeegee seen to have flyers (5)
16 Picture clue

DOWN

1 Picture clue
2 Sidestreet farewell, said as covering reason (5)
3 Tut, old airfield concealed it (3)
4 Picture clue
5 Harden thin urethane edging (5)
6 Picture clue
10 Picture clue
12 Pair of fivers, say, for singer (5)
13 Peer over the point and congratulate self (5)
15 Anchor man at the pitch? (3)

ACROSS

1a. Shocking noise! (7,3)

9a. Making a stink (7,4)

11a. Takings - less costs (3,8)

16a. Gingerbread roll? (10)

DOWN

1d. Precursor (10)

4d. Pasta (7)

6d. Nod off (4,6)

10d. Peninsular type (7)

ACROSS

1 Picture clue
5 Picture clue
8 A loss, adjusted (ropey!) (5)
9 Little professor has nothing to show for evidence (5)
10 I drink, I say, like windscreens in winter (3,2)
12 Slightly odd angle, being Heavenly (5)
14 Picture clue
15 Picture clue

DOWN

1 Picture clue
2 Rogues losing turn can be monsters! (5)
3 Greet that infernal duck! (5)
4 Picture clue
6 Picture clue
7 Picture clue
11 Mistake to go wrong alternatively (5)
13 Game, stupidly left with a shine (5)

ACROSS

1a. White flower (5,6)

5a. Emu worker (3,4)

14a. What spokes do to shine? (7)

15a. They'll lighten your walk (6,5)

DOWN

1d. Not daft islands to live on! (6,5)

4d. Piety (11)

6d. Let fall (7)

7d. North of Stockholm (7)

PITCHERWITS 3

ACROSS

1 Picture clue
5 Flypast said to be worse than a cold (3)
6 It's definitely an article! (3)
7 Picture clue
10 Mat's back for Scottish topper (3)
11 Awkwardly we run by Berkshire racecourse (7)
12 Second letter addition (3)
13 Picture clue
16 Water travel - as kings do (a bit) (3)
17 Pinch a bit of a drink (3)
18 Picture clue

DOWN

1 Picture clue
2 Must be sediment - else it's confused (4)
3 Healthy water source? (4)
4 Picture clue
5 Picture clue
8 Make babble part of meat dish (5)
9 Picture clue
14 Work to address the cat? (4)
15 Two slow pieces to be seen in Norway (4)

ACROSS

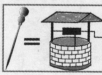
1a. ...that ends well (3,2,4)

7a. Lurked (7)

13a. Sri Lankan harbour (7)

18a. Basic painting (5,4)

DOWN

1d. Seasonal (8)

4d. Ability to take charge (10)

5d. ...for feast for prodigal (6,4)

9d. Main aspect (3,5)

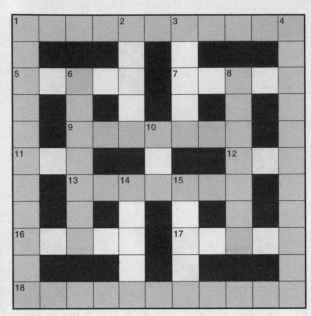

ACROSS

1 Picture clue
5 Fruit that could be sole fish (5)
7 Airline welcome - bit handy for the flight! (5)
9 Picture clue
11 Employment in warehouse (3)
12 Cambridgeshire city to rely on, at last (3)
13 Picture clue
16 Greetings from Hades? Next to nothing! (5)
17 Twentieth, without a bit of belief (5)
18 Picture clue

DOWN

1 Picture clue
2 Indulge bear's reputation (5)
3 Branched out of cattle farm (5)
4 Picture clue
6 Picture clue
8 Picture clue
10 Footie Campbell - a Roman sun-god? (3)
14 Workings rigged out - somehow aware (5)
15 Following a fret? Disturbing! (5)

ACROSS

1a. Re-words (11)

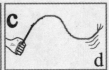

9a. Disagreed (7)

13a. San Francisco port (7)

18a. Alleyways (11)

DOWN

1d. Don't thump so hard! (4,7)

4d. Shelf lives over (4,2,5)

6d. Ace limo (maybe) (4,3)

8d. ...all guns blazing (5,2)

PITCHERWITS 3

ACROSS

1 Picture clue

7 Picture puzzle about transport (5)

8 Picture clue

11 Urn he broke as an Indian statesman (5)

13 Punt I made as a contribution (5)

14 Picture clue

16 Serious place to rest? (5)

18 Picture clue

DOWN

2 Sorbet will not set as a ball (3)

3 Picture clue

4 Trip, said to have ripped (4)

5 Picture clue

6 Picture clue

9 Picture clue

10 Outing in pin-stripe clothing (4)

12 French one at the Bull's Head? (4)

15 Fashionable central heating rules! (4)

17 Atmosphere of stairwell (3)

ACROSS

1a. Pointing out (10)

8a. Fractional city area? (7)

14a. 'Abe' - in E Midlands? (7)

18a. Separate with a wrench (5,5)

DOWN

3d. 'orrible little biter! (8)

5d. Ensures (10)

6d. Continental bread (6,4)

9d. Totalling (6,2)

ACROSS

1 Picture clue

5 Picture clue

8 Weight, right on cue (5)

9 Pup, in pose as glamour pic. (3-2)

10 Mad caper? Now let's have a summary (5)

12 Annoyed by dire mess around w/e (5)

14 Picture clue

15 Picture clue

DOWN

1 Picture clue

2 Northumbrian king who wined ridiculously (5)

3 Burn a sort myth (5)

4 Picture clue

6 Picture clue

7 Picture clue

11 Small wood, allegedly from the police (5)

13 Gecko, Dakotans hold to be film (5)

ACROSS

1a. Where to write your price? (4,7)

5a. Laundry gear (7)

14a. Swore to give up booze? (7)

15a. Topping , Holmes! (11)

DOWN

1d. You must be mad! (3,4,4)

4d. Spent the night (7,4)

6d. Church, in part (7)

7d. Best bit of a pizza? (7)

PITCHERWITS 3

ACROSS

1 Picture clue
5 Wagon to go out looking pale (3)
6 Antelope gun explodes (3)
7 Picture clue
10 Spanish sun - not against a parasol (3)
11 Sir, in no way can this be captivity (2,5)
12 Sweet, but no way is it tiny (3)
13 Picture clue
16 Behaviour, ultimately down to us (3)
17 Thanks said for road glue (3)
18 Picture clue

DOWN

1 Picture clue
2 Egg from a Roman breakfast? (4)
3 Burglar's haul made him swagger a bit (4)
4 Picture clue
5 Picture clue
8 Personal bloodline (or at a puzzle?) (5)
9 Picture clue
14 Old bird - something of a double act? (4)
15 No hip op. for the Shoshone (4)

ACROSS

1a. Spraying (9)

7a. Thanet town (7)

13a. Jezebel opponent (7)

18a. Unrecognisable! (9)

DOWN

1d. Chartreuse flavour (8)

4d. Country warden (10)

5d. One of your loyal ones, Ma'am? (5,5)

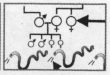
9d. Be responsible to (6,2)

ACROSS

1 Picture clue

5 Picture clue

7 Somewhat raw, left in a bit of fish (5)

8 Have left in the division by two (5)

9 Foolishly, I lent it to the cove (5)

11 Buffalo damaged bin so.... (5)

12 Picture clue

13 Picture clue

DOWN

1 Picture clue

2 Thrash about - as I take a bad fall (5)

3 Where rabbits move up along the bench? (5)

4 Picture clue

5 Picture clue

6 Picture clue

10 'Belongs to them' claim in that place (5)

11 Consecrate bighead - when smaller! (5)

ACROSS

1a. ...so will come to no harm (2,4,5)

5a. Begin (5,2)

12a. During which (7)

13a. Never got this before! (6,5)

DOWN

1d. Vanishing mode (4,4,3)

4d. E.g. trebuchet (5,6)

5d. Get it down your neck! (7)

6d. ...to a layby, say (5,2)

PITCHERWITS 3

ACROSS

1 Picture clue
5 Picture clue
9 Stew veg. found in crook rafter (4)
10 She's a German of bluff raucousness (4)
11 Humdrum ballet in centre-dance (5)
12 Where the officers eat sloppily? (4)
14 Got a bad classic tunic (4)
15 Picture clue
18 Picture clue

DOWN

1 Picture clue
2 Picture clue
3 Snake-like party leader (3)
4 In court, will she go for you? (3)
6 West Kensington site of original games? (7)
7 Is teacher a knight? (3)
8 Picture clue
10 Picture clue
13 Ask if it's got snow travel (3)
16 Steal, somewhat improbably (3)
17 Run? Good, first it's a farewell (3)

ACROSS

1a. Big suckers? (3,7)

5a. Put forward (8)

15a. Card game - for exam cheats? (8)

18a. Buzzer's a pest (10)

DOWN

1d. Involuntary (9)

2d. Aspirin remedy for duos (2,5)

8d. Furniture with rhythm? (9)

10d. Most plump (7)

ACROSS

1 Picture clue
5 Picture clue
9 Dumb location of axis (4)
10 Finally, surely, on what one can depend? (4)
11 Frequently seen in softeners (5)
12 Norway's boss featuring in school average (4)
13 Miscellany found at back of portfolio (4)
14 Picture clue
16 Picture clue
15 Consume, in time at least... (3)

DOWN

1 Picture clue
2 Hampered by a bit of a current (3)
3 Swop player on way up to transport (3)
4 Picture clue
6 Picture clue
7 To men of mystery, they're servants (7)
8 Picture clue
14 Cooker based on gossip? (3)

ACROSS

1a. For removing Sir's scribbles (5,6)

5a. They're built off-site (7)

14a. Little grain... (7)

16a. Confused (11)

DOWN

1d. Aristocratic (11)

4d. As shown by yawn.... (5,3,3)

6d. Refurbish and get better (7)

8d. Tawny-white flyer (4,3)

PITCHERWITS 3

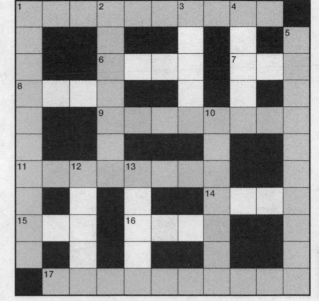

ACROSS

1 Picture clue
6 Jousting - has no guts to unite (4)
7 Singer Reed, from Cloud Nine (3)
8 It's you back, then? (4)
9 Picture clue
11 Picture clue
14 Rapt attention can be a snare (4)
15 Lair to end in disaster (3)
16 Alleviate fifths, so to speak (4)
17 Picture clue

DOWN

1 Picture clue
2 Picture clue
3 Icon I re-drew as atomic (5)
4 He'll obviously front the greeting (5)
5 Picture clue
10 Picture clue
12 Get in! (Somehow colour slightly) (5)
13 Transcend cans taken in general direction (5)

ACROSS

1a. Reform - unswervingly? (2,8)

9a. ...being educated, hopefully! (2,6)

11a. Tea-pot, so made as to be veg (8)

17a. Big Chief Sealer? (4,6)

DOWN

1d. Molluscs (10)

2d. Mexican city (7)

5d. Totally detailed account (4,6)

10d. Flighty stewardess? (7)

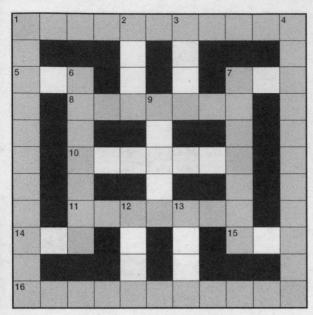

ACROSS

1 Picture clue
5 Formerly looked back (3)
7 Smooth bit of talking, you cow! (3)
8 Picture clue
10 Travel - through section of text? (7)
11 Picture clue
14 A week of wonder! (3)
15 Centrifugally yielded atmosphere (3)
16 Picture clue

DOWN

1 Picture clue
2 Den has 20% less flair (4)
3 Persona non grata to be uncovered soon (4)
4 Picture clue
6 Picture clue
7 Picture clue
9 Tones that jar at the start (5)
12 Iris to insulate strongly? (4)
13 Leave out motion with no pattern (4)

ACROSS

1a. Watchful lawmen (5,6)

8a. Canada's biggest (7)

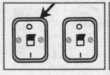

11a. Not included (4,3)

16a. Can they be a draw? (11)

DOWN

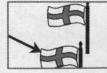

1d. It's poor! (3,8)

4d. Broker loan (5,6)

6d. Dotty brushwork? (7)

7d. Begin to travel (4,3)

PITCHERWITS 3

ACROSS

1 Picture clue
5 Picture clue
9 Cook ratatouille - with a bit of veg. (4)
10 Not long now, etc. (4)
11 Dance carved out from amboyna (5)
12 Look back to see the best (4)
14 Close to the line around the middle (4)
15 Picture clue
18 Picture clue

DOWN

1 Picture clue
2 Picture clue
3 Donkey's a bit biassed... (3)
4 Swooned in court (3)
6 Washington capitol where they have games? (7)
7 Rambo obviously gives a bit of disapproval (3)
8 Picture clue
10 Picture clue
13 Spartan location for a level (3)
16 Bit of research that's not straight? (3)
17 Obtain, somewhat energetically (3)

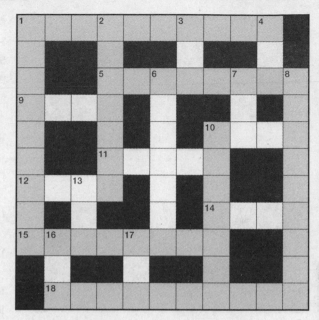

ACROSS

1a. Most... (3,3,1,3)

5a. Weapon to bolt with? (8)

15a. Cribbage, say (4,4)   18a. Rabbit (10)

DOWN

1d. Taken for granted (9)

2d. Makes tranquil (7)

8d. Just marvellous! (9)

10d. Mended speed with least said (7)

PITCHERWITS 3

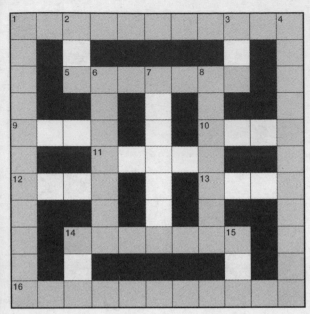

ACROSS

1 Picture clue
5 Picture clue
9 High-pitched cry of the old, old record (4)
10 Door state can be one of glass (4)
11 Forerunner of the repeat (2-3)
12 Ormolu does cut it as a game (4)
13 Fairish bit of the flag (4)
14 Picture clue
16 Picture clue

DOWN

1 Picture clue
2 Fair kiss can irritate inwardly (3)
3 Consume in the amphitheatre (3)
4 Picture clue
6 Picture clue
7 A gerbil chewed up the angel! (7)
8 Picture clue
14 Catch a wipe (3)
15 Two and nine, starting skin colour (3)

ACROSS

1a. Generate "Hooray!" (5,1,5)

5a. Most loathsome one (4,3)

14a. He's well grounded (7)

16a. Stretchers (6,5)

DOWN

1d. He'll try to score... (5,6)

4d. Never sold so many! (6,5)

6d. Get better (7)

8d. He died 'cos he lied! (7)

PITCHERWITS 3

ACROSS

1 Picture clue
7 Love the space that's eggy! (5)
8 Flag taken to hothead - as whiskey! (5)
9 Picture clue
11 Picture clue
14 Earls taken by light beam (5)
15 Figure of speech - at end of tight-rope! (5)
16 Picture clue

DOWN

1 Picture clue
2 Scam (ongoing) is part surrounded by... (5)
3 Antique stuffed in a folder (3)
4 Picture clue
5 Dobson ain't a pushover! (5)
6 Picture clue
10 Picture clue
12 Wing is more than a bit of a 'device' (5)
13 Score off rebound within - it's not on! (2-3)
15 Pair as well, so they say (3)

ACROSS

1a. Help a lot... (2,1,4,3)

9a. Wearying ache (7,4)

11a. Perfectly punctual (5,2,4)

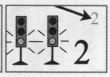
16a. Oversteps the mark (4,3,3)

DOWN

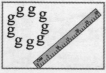
1d. Basic 'law' (6,4)

4d. Continuing... (5,2)

6d. Shift that stick! (6,4)

10d. Alternately (2,5)

ACROSS

1 Picture clue

5 Picture clue

8 Timer reset (in brief) (5)

9 Acrobat heads out to swim (5)

10 Harvest a crop from dried coconut (5)

12 Egg-store has nothing to change (5)

14 Picture clue

15 Picture clue

13 On the plus side, it's a snake... (5)

DOWN

1 Picture clue

2 Met, to arrange an emblem (5)

3 Tiepin I lost (so clumsy!) (5)

4 Picture clue

6 Picture clue

7 Picture clue

11 Lace edging? Strange topic! (5)

ACROSS

1a. Social behaviour (11)

5a. NE Italian place (7)

14a. Moved on board (7)

15a. What the lie does.... (3,4,4)

DOWN

1d. Teaching (11)

4d. Tot story (7,4)

6d. Places for post (2-5)

7d. Earth - deep down (7)

PITCHERWITS 3

ACROSS

1 Picture clue
5 Lie about a prophet... (3)
6 It is a groove, in truth (3)
7 Picture clue
10 She's got an aid package (3)
11 Crazy horn to add to S Wales (7)
12 She's into piezoelectricity! (3)
13 Picture clue
16 A bit scared to exist (3)
17 Relieve from horrid finale (3)
18 Picture clue

DOWN

1 Picture clue
2 Mongrel is a bit smutty (4)
3 Ancient city - where gold is weighed ? (4)
4 Picture clue
5 Picture clue
8 Atomic sort of Greek architecture? (5)
9 Picture clue
14 Sagacious - said belonging to 'Y' (4)
15 Agatha had a bit of a laugh... (2-2)

ACROSS

1a. Owning up to (9)

7a. Morsel (4,3)

13a. It's at Orwell's estuary (7)

18a. Marine savers (9)

DOWN

1d. Flighty prices? (8)

4d. It's yellow - and weedy! (10)

5d. Ovoid (-ish) (10)

9d. Original space heaters? (8)

PITCHERWITS 3

ACROSS

1 Picture clue
5 Fine metal peer? (5)
7 He's affected by badly written prose (5)
9 Picture clue
11 Aim to produce finale (3)
12 Bird is a bit unconstitutional! (3)
13 Picture clue
16 Sentimental sort of peas? (5)
17 Thundering reduces below (5)
18 Picture clue

DOWN

1 Picture clue
2 Get a rest from the 'fib-protest'? (3-2)
3 Dad heads up West for fruit (5)
4 Picture clue
6 Picture clue
8 Picture clue
10 Dragon - from the past (3)
14 By me, a crazy solution perhaps? (5)
15 Take over unlawfully in pursuit? It's not bad (5)

ACROSS

1a. Horsey ways? (6,5)

9a. 'Legged it' (3,4)

13a. Resort to East Devon? (7)

18a. Meal do (6,5)

DOWN

1d. Stretchy leaps of faith? (6,5)

4d. Community bash (6,5)

6d. Edges (7)

8d. Cut down (7)

PITCHERWITS 3

ACROSS

1 Picture clue

7 Pale, but with less weight (5)

8 Picture clue

11 Rind I trimmed for lemur (5)

13 Irritable in an unfortunate style (5)

14 Picture clue

16 Decorate fuss given to Royal Navy (5)

18 Picture clue

DOWN

2 Horse forever getting at you? (3)
3 Picture clue
4 Toffee, part eaten by posh type (4)
5 Picture clue

6 Picture clue
9 Picture clue
10 Soup recipe is quite a work (4)
12 Soft wood - or no soft wood? (4)

15 Tear, perhaps, of reduction (4)
17 Have some of the Crown Jewels (3)

ACROSS

1a. Bewitching (10)

8a. With which to tread the internet? (7)

14a. ...as an example? (5,2)

18a. Brewing preparation (3-7)

DOWN

3d. Starts car keylessly! (8)

5d. Very pleasing (10)

6d. ...like a successful pilot? (6,4)

9d. Offensive group (4,4)

ACROSS

1 Picture clue

5 Picture clue

8 Sierra Leone-speak in urban turmoil (5)

9 Conjure up artless take-over plan (5)

10 Steer around flavouring compound (5)

12 Fauntleroy allergy - a bit like a king (5)

14 Picture clue

15 Picture clue

DOWN

1 Picture clue

2 Just in case sites are gone - mixed spice will do (5)

3 Bigwig looking into Inuit home (5)

4 Picture clue

6 Picture clue

7 Picture clue

11 Gemstone - a summit from end to end, literally (5)

13 Funny ode leaves bits off, as singing style (5)

ACROSS

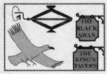

1a. Cruel Sea star (4,7)

5a. Narcissus (7)

14a. 'Nicked' (7)

15a. Beach homes (5,6)

DOWN

1d. He's got out! (11)

4d. Handy - and posh (5,6)

6d. Particle (7)

7d. Reveal (7)

PITCHERWITS 3

ACROSS

1 Picture clue
5 ...because it's a little lettuce (3)
6 A bit thick-skinned for snow-travel (3)
7 Picture clue
10 ...and not a bit abnormally! (3)
11 Apprentice eater - in discomfort! (7)
12 Bill's mate hiding in aircooler (3)
13 Picture clue
16 I'm a bit categorical... (3)
17 Bothering to get rid of tedious article (3)
18 Picture clue

DOWN

1 Picture clue
2 Leave out for the rubbish (4)
3 Look up a spot of the best (4)
4 Picture clue
5 Picture clue
8 Run out of Origanum - odd for Spanish pal! (5)
9 Picture clue
14 See a way to alleviate (4)
15 Even so, one is abominable (4)

ACROSS

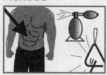
1a. Not being there (9)

7a. Text piece (7)

13a. Del Trotter, say (4,3)

18a. OTT (9)

DOWN

1d. Mixed (8)

4d. It's not painted this colour! (10)

5d. Everywhere in district (10)

9d. Story (8)

PUZZLE 175

PITCHERWITS 3

ACROSS

1 Picture clue

5 Picture clue

7 Drink aimed at single short street (5)

8 You think it starts with young people? (5)

9 Folded towel shows little winger (5)

11 Scowl horribly at bonnets (5)

12 Picture clue

13 Picture clue

DOWN

1 Picture clue

2 Sub, about to turn (1-4)

3 Doom is up at end of May - temperamental! (5)

4 Picture clue

5 Picture clue

6 Picture clue

10 Full of flavour - not as typified by inclusion (5)

11 Cancel loss, to shorten instrument (5)

ACROSS

1a. Get set forerunner (2,4,5)

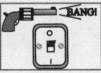

5a. Raced away (4,3)

12a. Show (7)

13a. ...just need to re-heat (5-6)

DOWN

1d. Could be sold... (4,2,5)

4d. Below Cook Strait (5,6)

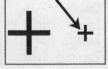

5d. For a little seller? (5,2)

6d. Could be split type.... (4-3)

PITCHERWITS 3

ACROSS

1 Picture clue
5 Picture clue
9 Amicable bit of mineral! (4)
10 Stratagem used in employment (4)
11 Parroter, apt to leave out bad mistake (5)
12 Amphibian - with digits, allegedly (4)
14 Pose ridiculously as currency (4)
15 Picture clue
18 Picture clue

DOWN

1 Picture clue
2 Picture clue
3 House at end of exercise (3)
4 Woman who's out of blusher... (3)
6 Insures scheme for daybreak (7)
7 Slippery type - could be shocking! (3)
8 Picture clue
10 Picture clue
13 Canada goose (in the past) (3)
16 Bit of old cloth? It's a tease! (3)
17 Icon, about to lose molecule (3)

ACROSS

1a. Now they are 2 down! (5-5)

5a. For a tidy water supply (4,4)

15a. Sticks to bishops? (8)

18a. Cavies (6,4)

DOWN

1d. Giving souls to nature (9)

2d. Like a horseshoe (nearly!) (1-6)

8d. Idle oafs (9)

10d. Supports (5,2)

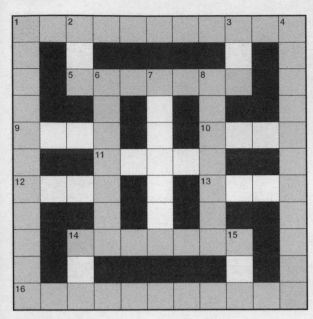

ACROSS

1 Picture clue
5 Picture clue
9 Ventilated section of fairylights (4)
10 Stun doctor into revealing ruin (4)
11 As aim goes, it's a Kenyan tribe (5)
12 How to walk like old Lettuce (4)
13 Tennessee player in slow leak (4)
14 Picture clue
16 Picture clue

DOWN

1 Picture clue
2 Heard little motor could cut grass (3)
3 Be situated in order to deceive (3)
4 Picture clue
6 Picture clue
7 Learning points - from the lectern? (7)
8 Picture clue
14 Use some skittles for equipment (3)
15 Bath in this patch... (3)

ACROSS

1a. Top chats? (6,5)

5a. Aspiring (5-2)

14a. German kings (7)

16a. Shopping industry? (6,5)

DOWN

1d. Appropriate to (8,3)

4d. For top scholar (6,5)

6d. Games place (original)! (7)

8d. Samson-type (7)

PITCHERWITS 3

ACROSS

1 Picture clue
6 Approach to earn, roughly (4)
7 Model-sounding drink (3)
8 Chance to be a lady? (4)
9 Picture clue
11 Picture clue
14 Was once the thing - way out! (4)
15 Crowd minding own business, initially (3)
16 Keen on some of main topic (4)
17 Picture clue

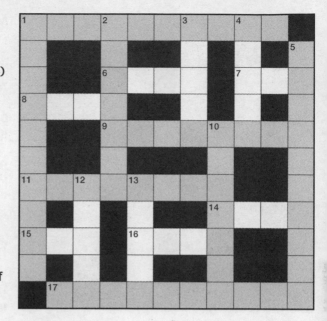

DOWN

1 Picture clue
2 Picture clue
3 Roman design for Marilyn Monroe (5)
4 Altogether now for the..."Frutti lolly!" (5)
5 Picture clue
10 Picture clue
12 Ablution a lot less muddled in old N African country (5)
13 Bribery - but not by a wild rose! (5)

ACROSS

1a. Brotherhood (10)

9a. Flying (8)

11a. Manual (not automatic) (8)

17a. By all means... (4,2,4)

DOWN

1d. Be at ease (4,2,4)

2d. Drinker's pot (7)

5d. Early reconnaissance (4,6)

10d. Start of 9 across (4-3)

PITCHERWITS 3

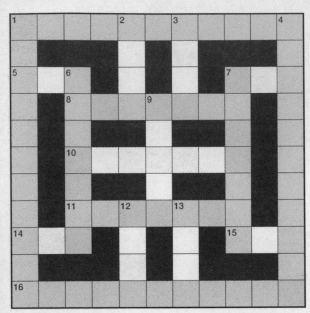

ACROSS

1 Picture clue
5 Short doze on snooker table (3)
7 Disapproval - of Booker Prize? (3)
8 Picture clue
10 Living with a big din - awful! (7)
11 Picture clue
14 Take in something of Poet Laureate's (3)
15 The stuff we breathed (allegedly) before (3)
16 Picture clue

DOWN

1 Picture clue
2 Void partner has no legal force (4)
3 Blood line not straight from the vine (4)
4 Picture clue
6 Picture clue
7 Picture clue
9 Helped adenoid, lacking no alterations (5)
12 Lovely fruit, but hideous allegedly (4)
13 Brainchild, a bit slow to move (4)

ACROSS

1a. Firm opinions (6,5)

8a. Georgia's biggest (7)

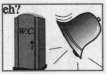

11a. Escaping (7)

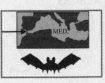

16a. Cricketing style (8,3)

DOWN

1d. Crustaceans (11)

4d. Northern twang (5,6)

6d. Roof wall (7)

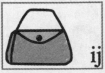

7d. Cases (7)

PITCHERWITS 3

ACROSS

1 Picture clue
5 Picture clue
9 Page of plants? (4)
10 Stifles back end of ego (4)
11 Smallest to be rented, apparently (5)
12 False god has little identity, but nothing left (4)
14 Positive sign - just as well! (4)
15 Picture clue
18 Picture clue

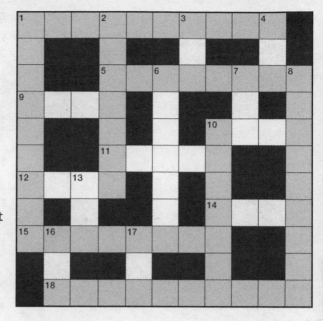

DOWN

1 Picture clue
2 Picture clue
3 Purpose is a bit obtuse (3)
4 What jelly did for TV? (3)
6 Sara, I'm a bit shaken up by old Middle Israel (7)
7 Draw in ambiguities (3)
8 Picture clue
10 Picture clue
13 What's said of us in 60 mins (3)
16 Fire remains washed out (3)
17 Pair of designs (unlike one's initials) (3)

ACROSS

1a. Old poor places (10)

5a. Agree with (6,2)

15a. Bad times (4,4)

18a. It's squared, to sum up… (10)

DOWN

1d. Needed for Pitcherwits! (5,4)

2d. Pike that's a peak! (7)

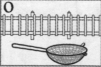

8d. Rude (9)

10d. Stays inside (5,2)

PITCHERWITS 3

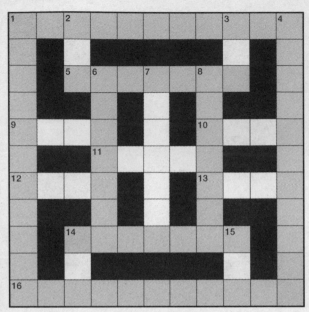

ACROSS

1 Picture clue

5 Picture clue

9 Inform if loss of the usual (4)

10 A real beginning to space (4)

11 Carp has answer for 'chippy' (5)

12 Carry the animal (4)

13 Care for seat of thinking (4)

14 Picture clue

16 Picture clue

DOWN

1 Picture clue

2 Donkey is like a stop-start (3)

3 Tree to sing about – very wet! (3)

4 Picture clue

6 Picture clue

7 Obnoxious gnat bit in (7)

8 Picture clue

14 Pair to be arduously trimmed (3)

15 Much to be sold under hammer (3)

ACROSS

1a. Reducing pro rata (7,4)

5a. ...and waited (3,4)

14a. She's no boarder! (3,4)

16a. Piecrust stuff (5,6)

DOWN

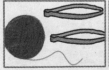

1d. No brass players, then? (6,5)

4d. Spick and span (4,3,4)

6d. Spanish city (7)

8d. Smooth talker? (7)

PITCHERWITS 3

ACROSS

1 Picture clue
7 Pot plant returned with accuracy, but no car! (5)
8 Occur as a one-off increase (5)
9 Picture clue
11 Picture clue
14 Blind padre is in difficulties (5)
15 Modify commercial apartment, small (5)
16 Picture clue

DOWN

1 Picture clue
2 Clear report of Sid being with Lou, right ? (5)
3 It's an age of base rates... (3)
4 Picture clue
5 I bail out - as an excuse (5)
6 Picture clue
10 Picture clue
12 Fertilizer found in Antigua, normally (5)
13 Mix up with IQ Air of Baghdad (5)
15 Help in braiding... (3)

ACROSS

1a. Past-it actor (6,4)

9a. Sounds signally important! (5,6)

11a. Haute couture (4,7)

16a. Tainted grapejuice (6,4)

DOWN

1d. Little hairy flowers (3,7)

4d. Sticky flower bits? (7)

6d. Reel move? (4-3-3)

10d. Not highest rates (3-4)

PITCHERWITS 3

ACROSS

1 Picture clue

5 Picture clue

8 Loner must reform to register (5)

9 Royal pop group? (5)

10 In a mainframe, it's sort of red (5)

12 Florida homes - in such a state! (5)

14 Picture clue

15 Picture clue

DOWN

1 Picture clue

2 Advisory day out to be looked through (5)

3 Unease, without a pattern to follow (5)

4 Picture clue

6 Picture clue

7 Picture clue

11 If gun went off, there'd be mushrooms (5)

13 A duo I made into visual accompaniment (5)

ACROSS

1a. Passion papers? (4,7)

5a. Bible writers (7)

14a. Anti-slip (3-4)

15a. Specifying (7,4)

DOWN

1d. He beat Columbus by 500 years! (4,7)

4d. Start (3,2,6)

6d. Take on board again (7)

7d. Hurry! (2,5)

PITCHERWITS 3

ACROSS

1 Picture clue
5 Wearying illness said to have gone quickly (3)
6 Draw partner for shirt (3)
7 Picture clue
10 Back-chat of a kisser? (3)
11 Eccentric major - 50-50 chance of being a pud! (3,4)
12 Molecule in position (3)
13 Picture clue
16 Had supper, say, in a bit of a state (3)
17 Managed to sprint in the past.... (3)
18 Picture clue

DOWN

1 Picture clue
2 More than finished! (4)
3 Fancy another bit of colour? (4)
4 Picture clue
5 Picture clue
8 Steed said to croak? (5)
9 Picture clue
14 Limb located in axis of countries (4)
15 Herbwise, it could be either (4)

ACROSS

1a. Bringing forth (not fifth) (9)

7a. Answer's in S Wales (7)

13a. 'Spouses' (7)

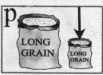

18a. Invaluably comical? (9)

DOWN

1d. Way to hang a picture? (3-2,3)

4d. No worries! (3,7)

5d. Seems tacky (5,5)

9d. Gives birth (8)

PITCHERWITS 3

ACROSS

1 Picture clue
5 Self-less feudalist sorts out review (5)
7 Blood line has a rota error (5)
9 Picture clue
11 Wonder claimed for a mineral (3)
12 Use pastel mauve to outline tree (3)
13 Picture clue
16 FInally announce weight (5)
17 Emblem would pester with right ending (5)
18 Picture clue

DOWN

1 Picture clue
2 Dish of tripe? Ugh! (5)
3 Want rough force to have a nasal sound (5)
4 Picture clue
6 Picture clue
8 Picture clue
10 Perverse one attributed to Sod - or Murphy! (3)
14 Later taken to be on the ball (5)
15 Claim Buenos Airean is a bit of a soak (5)

ACROSS

1a. Lotteries (11)

9a. Lung, in a bad way for explosive hammer (7)

13a. Illustration (7)

18a. Degenerate (2,2,3,4)

DOWN

1d. Strain a welcome? (4,3,4)

4d. Miniatures (5,6)

6d. New Zealand place (7)

8d. Went back on (7)

PITCHERWITS 3

ACROSS

1. Picture clue
7. Spur madly after turn unlawfully to seize (5)
8. Picture clue
11. Tortilla found from within a choice selection (5)
13. She's an aid in trouble all right! (5)
14. Picture clue
16. Unmanly - not my way to invalidate (5)
18. Picture clue

DOWN

2. Little coin from the South (3)
3. Picture clue
4. Cane was cut to be fresh (4)
5. Picture clue
6. Picture clue
9. Picture clue
10. Old bit of tragedy (4)
12. Pieces of stucco date the finale (4)
15. Airs composed for Hindu lady - to wear? (4)
17. Pass can up to fool (3)

ACROSS

1a. Can be overcome (10)

8a. Rouse again (7)

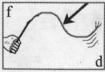
14a. Showed off (7)

18a. Royal body process (3,2,5)

DOWN

3d. Advance (8)

5d. Ladder type (10)

6d. West African bird (6,4)

9d. Plentiful (8)

ACROSS

1 Picture clue

5 Picture clue

8 Dotty kind of dance? (5)

9 Thread of free verse (5)

10 Calendar fruits? (5)

12 Inaccurate not to unite this city in Ghana (5)

14 Picture clue

15 Picture clue

13 Poor copy to turn water-rat (5)

DOWN

1 Picture clue

2 Ear-like arousal? - not so unlikely! (5)

3 Dig, in model version (5)

4 Picture clue

6 Picture clue

7 Picture clue

11 Forbidden the 'OO' label, above... (5)

ACROSS

1a. Took in all (9,2)

5a. Peaceful (7)

14a. Courage (7)

15a. Fool about (5,6)

DOWN

1d. Don't need this at the back! (7,4)

4d. Went into lead (6,5)

6d. Was sane, sort of, in S Wales (7)

7d. Desert (7)

PITCHERWITS 3

ACROSS

1 Picture clue
5 Adherents of that woman (3)
6 Dispose of horrid finale (3)
7 Picture clue
10 Managed to sprint yesterday (3)
11 Pub's rug design to say 'food's ready' (5,2!)
12 Splits in half of the object (3)
13 Picture clue
16 Some prophet to be made from Bakelite... (3)
17 Visual agreement put on back-to-front (3)
18 Picture clue

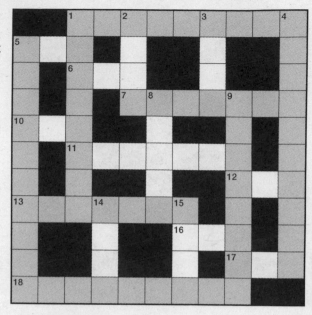

DOWN

1 Picture clue
2 Sundays, without any froth (4)
3 VIP's, up for a 'wide boy' (4)
4 Picture clue
5 Picture clue
8 Glib elaboration? - paper malice at heart (5)
9 Picture clue
14 Copy, but a sound one (4)
15 Half a home? (4)

ACROSS

1a. Cutting off (9)

7a. Splinters (7)

13a. Trials (7)

18a. Loathing (9)

DOWN

1d. Set up (8)

4d. Grows beyond harvesting (4,2,4)

5d. In On Golden Pond - at last! (5,5)

9d. Running out (8)

PITCHERWITS 3

ACROSS

1 Picture clue

5 Picture clue

7 Tiber diverted for clan (5)

8 Be on cloud nine, in complex ultimatum (5)

9 12" happening (5)

11 Big looking-glass reveals snow home (5)

12 Picture clue

13 Picture clue

DOWN

1 Picture clue

2 Banana-skin anecdote - a bit mindless! (5)

3 After 12 o'clock, sweetheart, there's nobody (2-3)

4 Picture clue

5 Picture clue

6 Picture clue

10 Turn of events at the dance (5)

11 RSJ light enough for a screen? (1-4)

ACROSS

1a. View sampler (7,4)

5a. Grumpy (2,1,4)

12a. Spend it, roughly, to pay the vicar (7)

13a. Correct level (5,6)

DOWN

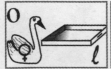

1d. It's pulled - without a top (4,7)

4d. It's got power to illuminate (5,6)

5d. Where villains used to be clapped (2,5)

6d. 'Twiced' (7)

ACROSS

1 Picture clue
5 Picture clue
9 Fine story, but part-depiction (4)
10 Hiawatha, happy to have a bit of a laugh (2-2)
11 Duo to try and exceed (5)
12 Press down current model first (4)
14 VIP's right, eh, 'wide boy'? (4)
15 Picture clue
18 Picture clue

DOWN

1 Picture clue
2 Picture clue
3 Foot is poor, but sound substitute (3)
4 Roman sun god - not against a parasol (3)
6 Wet it, or change it, but send a letter (5,2)
7 Ribonucleic acid that ran about (1,1,1)
8 Picture clue
10 Picture clue
13 Fool of the beaker people? (3)
16 By hook or by crook, got the ball (3)
17 Resistance - sounds quite meditative! (3)

ACROSS

1a. Invertebrates (10)

5a. It's way out West (3,5)

15a. Pattern (8)

18a. He's got a Fat Duck, starring.... (10)

DOWN

1d. Disaffected (9)

2d. It's got layer upon layer... (3,4)

8d. ...over what to forget... (4,1,4)

10d. Clever person (7)

PITCHERWITS 3

ACROSS

1 Picture clue
5 Picture clue
9 Currency that's de-railed maybe? (4)
10 Shunt off part of preposition (4)
11 Runner has mop-head following bunch of women (5)
12 Bargain event - in Cheshire? (4)
13 Fruity professor on board? (4)
14 Picture clue
16 Picture clue

DOWN

1 Picture clue
2 Marsh is a bit offensive (3)
3 Portrayal that sheds light (3)
4 Picture clue
6 Picture clue
7 Foodie can tug more out (7)
8 Picture clue
14 Sick of millions wasted (3)
15 Look up and down (3)

ACROSS

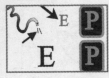

1a. Big game drive-throughs (6,5)

5a. ...but nice! (7)

14a. Copy I'm to take to single gallery (7)

16a. Great in salads! (4,7)

DOWN

1d. ...where one might find love (7,4)

4d. Where we learned to have dinners? (6,5)

6d. Disney place (7)

8d. Instrument to show off? (7)

PITCHERWITS 3

ACROSS

1 Picture clue
6 Label - it's personal! (4)
7 About as intelligent as a 2W bulb! (3)
8 Hollyhock is sure to have sweet gesture (4)
9 Picture clue
11 Picture clue
14 Succulent - it goes well with Vera (4)
15 Advice on a point.... (3)
16 Cajole the aerial lead? (4)
17 Picture clue

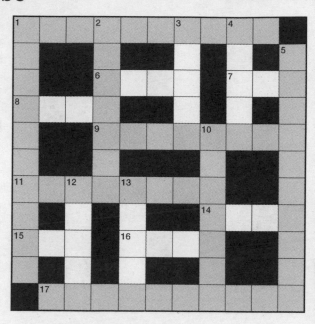

DOWN

1 Picture clue
2 Picture clue
3 Tense set-up for awkward years (5)
4 ...isn't out of auditions for visual accompaniment (5)
5 Picture clue
10 Picture clue
12 Out-of-step ideas - lukewarm (5)
13 Happen in havoc, currently (5)

ACROSS

1a. Side of stickers? (6,4)

9a. Big homes (8)

11a. Fail to impress (3,2,3)

17a. To whom things are sent (10)

DOWN

1d. Refer to past... (4,4,2)

2d. Relative (7)

5d. Entertainments (10)

10d. They help up glaciers (3,4)

PITCHERWITS 3

ACROSS

1 Picture clue
5 Puss, having bit of a panic attack (3)
7 Looked back and existed (3)
8 Picture clue
10 Endless teacupful designed as footie trophy (1,1,1,1,3)
11 Picture clue
14 Welcome Maria in extravert setting (3)
15 Spoil the front of the market (3)
16 Picture clue

DOWN

1 Picture clue
2 Thing is, it's a mite confused (4)
3 Rummage around inside for kit (4)
4 Picture clue
6 Picture clue
7 Picture clue
9 Quickly - it could be just one step (5)
12 Little corner is back on, alright? (4)
13 How renewables give you the bird (4)

ACROSS

1a. Failing (7,4)

8a. Where the Good guy comes from? (7)

11a. That's refreshing! (7)

16a. Brand - unused (8,3)

DOWN

1d. They were a Biblical waste of time! (6,5)

4d. Nothing to tie to it! (2,5,4)

6d. Got a right angle to it! (1-6)

7d. S American candle tree? (3,4)

PITCHERWITS 3

ACROSS

1 Picture clue
5 Picture clue
9 What are these objectionable flyers? (1,1,1,1)
10 Scorch character a bit (4)
11 Join in with golden rollover (5)
12 Leader is of them, I realise (4)
14 Excited a while back, by force (4)
15 Picture clue
18 Picture clue

DOWN

1 Picture clue
2 Picture clue
3 Seventh part of any ordinal (3)
4 Regret - such a bitter herb! (3)
6 Nervy sort not said to be an old Rhone (7)
7 Delilah ends up in scales (3)
8 Picture clue
10 Picture clue
13 Half-ration? - just a particle! (3)
16 Brilliant serve from the pack? (3)
17 Stern bit of water travel (3)

ACROSS

1a. He's got lots to sell... (10)

5a. Old camera lenses? (8)

15a. Queen Vic painter (8)

18a. Where the power's at! (6,4)

DOWN

1d. Have good boding? (5,4)

2d. Rip test to shreds for racing 'consultant' (7)

8d. Handle roughly (6-3)

10d. More lucid (7)

PITCHERWITS 3

ACROSS

1 Picture clue
5 Picture clue
9 I do loathe a bit of a false god (4)
10 Hay, say, that's freighted outright (4)
11 Salt turns back after a map collection (5)
12 'Wacky' - takes whole alphabet back to New York (4)
13 As always, she was first, right? (4)
14 Picture clue
16 Picture clue

DOWN

1 Picture clue
2 Neat work setting for duo (3)
3 'Local area network' - it's part of the language! (1,1,1)
4 Picture clue
6 Picture clue
7 Pitman has a dog, right? (7)
8 Picture clue
14 It's policy to be half frozen (3)
15 Little one to add up - and down! (3)

ACROSS

1a. ...to spread round on bread (11)

5a. It's 15th, in Greek (7)

14a. Legal responsibility (2,5)

16a. Shot up (11)

DOWN

1d. Comings of age (3,8)

4d. ...waiting (5,6)

6d. From an Asian peninsular (7)

8d. Puts to one side (7)

PITCHERWITS 3

ACROSS

1 Picture clue
7 Never taken to be cheek... (5)
8 Make foolish, when saddled centrally (5)
9 Picture clue
11 Picture clue
14 One is inclined to be sound... (5)
15 Hydrocarbon seen in town of Abernethy limits (5)
16 Picture clue

DOWN

1 Picture clue
2 Insect stage - from Etna, say? (5)
3 It's singularly royal! (3)
4 Picture clue
5 Asian republic appearing in diagram form (5)
6 Picture clue
10 Picture clue
12 Religious cooker? (5)
13 Doorkeeper from fabulous Herefordshire (5)
15 Time of geranium cutting (3)

ACROSS

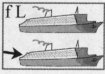
1a. Meeting together (10)

9a. ...as an apprentice, say (5,1,5)

11a. How does this work? (7,4)

16a. Old? ...or mature? (4-6)

DOWN

1d. End numbering (5,5)

4d. Washington's largest (7)

6d. Sparkly (10)

10d. Foolishly (7)

PITCHERWITS 3

ACROSS

1 Picture clue

5 Picture clue

8 Material in many, long-drawn-out pieces (5)

9 Panic, as tennis hides class (5)

10 It's got news of a feeble sort of tiger (5)

12 Where it's said to be, of them (5)

14 Picture clue

15 Picture clue

DOWN

1 Picture clue

2 This is a little bit of rope fibre (5)

3 Absolute zero - as is found in the desert. Well? (5)

4 Picture clue

6 Picture clue

7 Picture clue

11 I wept at ruined flyer (5)

13 Boredom of reunion (or not, maybe?) (5)

ACROSS

1a. Is this depressing? (7,4)

5a. It's the tops! (7)

14a. Continues (5,2)

15a. Logical-ness (11)

DOWN

1d. Medium, but not average (3,3,5)

4d. Eye, drawn, say, oddly at annual start (3,5,3)

6d. Ore (but not else!) (7)

7d. Provokes, say, understanding (7)

PITCHERWITS 3

ACROSS

1 Picture clue
5 Jump on one to make beer (3)
6 Prefix for the real expert (3)
7 Picture clue
10 ...and goes back to personal coding (1,1,1)
11 Orwell, I take to be more inferior (7)
12 Renovation uncovers eggs (3)
13 Picture clue
16 It's another name, initially (3)
17 House at end of employment (3)
18 Picture clue

DOWN

1 Picture clue
2 Shine, although hanging low, finally (4)
3 Discovery said to have been given a fixed penalty (4)
4 Picture clue
5 Picture clue
8 Leered, as Og took charge! (5)
9 Picture clue
14 Exhort surgeon to exclude relative (4)
15 Pudding was a good part of it... (4)

ACROSS

1a. Heavenly swimmer? (9)

7a. Only the bonfire remains... (4,3)

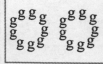

13a. Reasons for coffee? (7)

18a. To sell abroad (3,6)

DOWN

1d. Attract (6,2)

4d. Plaudits for pilots? (4,6)

5d. Waiting before doing (7,3)

9d. Flyer (8)

PITCHERWITS 3

ACROSS

1 Picture clue
5 Read the runes as hospital worker (5)
7 Tuna-fish has not got to be unsuitable (5)
9 Picture clue
11 Printing units - 13th in letter lists! (3)
12 Slippery one in three layers (3)
13 Picture clue
16 Would you believe it? God is ours (5)
17 Give a pup a training - in New Guinea (5)
18 Picture clue

DOWN

1 Picture clue
2 Connect with edition - do not muddle (3,2)
3 Words are nothing to 'conventional' types (5)
4 Picture clue
6 Picture clue
8 Picture clue
10 Twosome, assiduously pruned (3)
14 Primary trees at the end of August (5)
15 Guru, peeling away from currency (5)

ACROSS

1a. Held back (2,9)

9a. It's a house! (7)

13a. Tells (7)

18a. It's close! (4,3,4)

DOWN

1d. He's not guilty (8,3)

4d. Let fly - no inhibitions (3,4,4)

6d. Cocoons (3,4)

8d. Starts (5,2)

PITCHERWITS 3

ACROSS

1 Picture clue

7 Iron door reveals a dance (5)

8 Picture clue

11 She's an aid, confused (5)

13 Pretend it's foreign (or not!) (5)

14 Picture clue

16 Tear I make out to be angry (5)

18 Picture clue

DOWN

2 Tea store is burnt out (3)

3 Picture clue

4 Pudding was a good bit! (4)

5 Picture clue

6 Picture clue

9 Picture clue

10 Fruit presumably not grown for its looks (4)

12 Node, badly completed (4)

15 Waisted, but set out clumsily in gully (4)

17 Copy the orang-utan, say (3)

ACROSS

1a. With faith in mankind (10)

8a. Jumbo drivers take out a hot sum (7)

14a. Hair style (4,3)

18a. Masterminded (10)

DOWN

3d. Highly fragrant (8)

5d. Reference (5-5)

6d. Not of small proportions (5-5)

9d. Match middle (4-4)

1

ACROSS: 1 In and around, 5 Classic, 8 Inter, 9 Forms, 10 Ennui, 12 Rowel, 14 Ratchet, 15 One two three. DOWN: 1 Inquire into, 2 Ascot, 3 Ulcer, 4 Dead silence, 6 Airlift, 7 So forth, 11 Nerve, 13 Water.

2

ACROSS: 1 Care label, 5 Boa, 6 Rim, 7 Parable, 10 Ass, 11 Fairest, 12 Per, 13 Oarsman, 16 Our, 17 Tog, 18 Down tools. DOWN: 1 Cares for, 2 Romp, 3 Area, 4 Late Spring, 5 Breadboard, 8 Aorta, 9 Bit parts, 14 Shin, 15 No-go.

3

ACROSS: 1 Centripetal, 5 Nippy, 7 Repro, 9 Roe deer, 11 Oat, 12 Arc, 13 Inmates, 16 In-off, 17 Align, 18 Gearing down. DOWN: 1 Controlling, 2 Rhyme, 3 Puree, 4 Loose cannon, 6 Portico, 8 Paraski, 10 DNA, 14 Mufti, 15 Twang.

4

ACROSS: 1 Cool-headed, 7 Rifle, 8 Damping, 11 Tempo, 13 Nylon, 14 Candour, 16 Oasis, 18 Discarding. DOWN: 2 Oaf, 3 Lie doggo, 4 Atop, 5 Doggedness, 6 Protracted, 9 Main road, 10 Idol, 12 Mean, 15 Disc, 17 Sin.

5

ACROSS: 1 Bicarbonate, 5 Oil pipe, 8 Endow, 9 Set-up, 10 Irate, 12 After, 14 Marceau, 15 Geneva Bible. DOWN: 1 Brake lining, 2 Crowd, 3 Agent, 4 Escape route, 6 Low gear, 7 In spate, 11 Adman, 13 Thumb.

6

ACROSS: 1 Beersheba, 5 DNA, 6 Cue, 7 Railcar, 10 Ass, 11 Product, 12 Fat, 13 Ranking, 16 Ova, 17 Pen, 18 Encircles. DOWN: 1 Backspin, 2 Ever, 3 Hall, 4 Attraction, 5 Disapprove, 8 Add-on, 9 Catflaps, 14 Kiwi, 15 Goal.

7

ACROSS: 1 Bird fancier, 5 Redress, 7 Thump, 8 Sense, 9 Fraud, 11 Plumb, 12 B movies, 13 Pork pie hats. DOWN: 1 Be out of step, 2 Fed up, 3 Needs, 4 Runner beans, 5 Rhubarb, 6 Send-ups, 10 Droop, 11 Prime.

8

ACROSS: 1 Editorials, 5 Russians, 9 Ruin, 10 Gear, 11 Pacer, 12 Togs, 14 Wing, 15 Casts off, 18 Properties. DOWN: 1 Energetic, 2 Turn-ups, 3 Its, 4 Sun, 6 Stick to, 7 Ape, 8 Strangers, 10 Grow fat, 13 Gas, 16 Alp, 17 Sap.

9

ACROSS: 1 Landscaping, 5 Taken up, 9 Biro, 10 Rang, 11 Naomi, 12 Anti, 13 Gala, 14 Sensate, 16 Dispersions. DOWN: 1 Left-brained, 2 Not, 3 Imp, 4 Going halves, 6 Agonise, 7 Euro-MPs, 8 Upright, 14 S O S, 15 Ego.

10

ACROSS: 1 Daily paper, 6 Boar, 7 Nil, 8 Base, 9 Lunatics, 11 Cream tea, 14 Into, 15 Ice, 16 Rift, 17 Cause a riot. DOWN: 1 Double chin, 2 Lobelia, 3 Aorta, 4 Ennui, 5 Flashpoint, 10 Traitor, 12 Elena, 13 Mores.

11

ACROSS: 1 Constrained, 5 Nil, 7 Pig, 8 Exceeds, 10 Tendril, 11 Lunette, 14 Its, 15 Red, 16 Gross income. DOWN: 1 Conjugating, 2 Talc, 3 Aloe, 4 Doggy paddle, 6 Lentils, 7 Psalter, 9 Endue, 12 Nuts, 13 Town.

12

ACROSS: 1 Stretchers, 5 Repeated, 9 Trio, 10 Rosa, 11 Petri, 12 Acts, 14 Gulp, 15 Dead ends, 18 Antagonise.
DOWN: 1 Southward, 2 Euro-MPs, 3 Hoe, 4 Sue, 6 Pattern, 7 Two, 8 Drainpipe, 10 Rings in, 13 Tea, 16 Era, 17 Eva.

13

ACROSS: 1 Mistreating, 5 Goldman, 9 Idle, 10 Amen, 11 Sit-in, 12 Egad!, 13 Doff, 14 Meeting, 16 Hooded crows.
DOWN: 1 Machine wash, 2 Sag, 3 Ion, 4 Granny flats, 6 One's due, 7 Distort, 8 Abandon, 14 Moo, 15 Goo.

14

ACROSS: 1 Bottled out, 7 Orbit, 8 Wooed, 9 See you later, 11 Limit switch, 14 Eerie, 15 Water, 16 Boiled rice. DOWN: 1 Bookseller, 2 Table, 3 Let, 4 Dew-claw, 5 U-boat, 6 A dark horse, 10 Oatmeal, 12 Marco, 13 Tutti, 15 Wad.

15

ACROSS: 1 In a nutshell, 5 Piped up, 8 Swami, 9 Orlon, 10 No way, 12 Audio, 14 Isolate, 15 Legal tender. DOWN: 1 Inessential, 2 Alpha, 3 Expel, 4 Law and order, 6 Privy to, 7 Diorama, 11 Wring, 13 Dread.

16

ACROSS: 1 Whispered, 5 Boa, 6 Yet, 7 One offs, 10 Ova, 11 Rooster, 12 Sob, 13 Largely, 16 Era, 17 Its, 18 Glittered. DOWN: 1 Wayfarer, 2 Into, 3 Echo, 4 Dissembles, 5 Before long, 8 Nasal, 9 First Aid, 14 Gent, 15 Year.

17

ACROSS: 1 City council, 5 Offal, 7 Taboo, 9 Chaired, 11 Ore, 12 Mac, 13 Tornado, 16 Add up, 17 Olden, 18 Holiday home.
DOWN: 1 Choreograph, 2 Celia, 3 Utter, 4 Loose change, 6 Faceted, 8 Bad mood, 10 Inn, 14 Rapid, 15 Agony.

18

ACROSS: 1 Dreamy-eyed, 7 Indri, 8 Deluded, 11 Hover, 13 Tutti, 14 Ran into, 16 V-sign, 18 Downstroke. DOWN: 2 Rid, 3 Acid rain, 4 Ecru, 5 Dandelions, 6 Big-hearted, 9 Left-over, 10 Deft, 12 Vein, 15 Iron, 17 Ink.

19

ACROSS: 1 Demarcating, 5 Spectre, 8 Largo, 9 Often, 10 Astir, 12 Eaves, 14 Capered, 15 Go to the ball. DOWN: 1 Downloading, 2 Miser, 3 Inert, 4 Groundswell, 6 Ego trip, 7 Too near, 11 Tacit, 13 Vodka.

20

ACROSS: 1 Gone broke, 5 Car, 6 Elm, 7 Ergo sum, 10 Tea, 11 Roomful, 12 Lea, 13 Grating, 16 Out, 17 Odd, 18 Fair price. DOWN: 1 Grey area, 2 Name, 3 Re-do, 4 Eliminated, 5 Carting off, 8 Roman, 9 Sillitoe, 14 Tour, 15 Gobi.

21

ACROSS: 1 Lie on a level, 5 Saw sets, 7 Axial, 8 Elgin, 9 After, 11 Chino, 12 Cannery, 13 Doublethink. DOWN: 1 Long-awaited, 2 Newel, 3 Liege, 4 Learn to walk, 5 Sciatic, 6 Signify, 10 Renal, 11 Chert.

22

ACROSS: 1 Punch drunk, 5 Home-made, 9 Time, 10 Bloc, 11 Ester, 12 Nerd, 14 Over, 15 Downwind, 18 Down and out. DOWN: 1 Patterned, 2 Cohered, 3 Roe, 4 Kid, 6 Martini, 7 All, 8 Eucharist, 10 Brooded, 13 Raw, 16 Old, 17 Win.

23

ACROSS: 1 Trouble-free, 5 Thin ice, 9 Idea, 10 Roar, 11 Rapid, 12 Gawk, 13 Anti, 14 Entries, 16 In full spate. DOWN: 1 The King and I, 2 Out, 3 Rue, 4 Exterminate, 6 Hearken, 7 Nippier, 8 Cordate, 14 Elf, 15 Sea.

24

ACROSS: 1 Dissuasion, 6 Beer, 7 Tea, 8 Bide, 9 Rings off, 11 Properly, 14 Also, 15 Roe, 16 Seem, 17 Bar magnets. DOWN: 1 Double-park, 2 Sober up, 3 Shrug, 4 Outdo, 5 Half crowns, 10 Say amen, 12 Opera, 13 Epsom.

25

ACROSS: 1 Jockey wheel, 5 Cap, 7 Rig, 8 Abridge, 10 Adviser, 11 Element, 14 USA, 15 Eli, 16 Settlements. DOWN: 1 Jack of clubs, 2 Emir, 3 Ward, 4 Light duties, 6 Panacea, 7 Re-write, 9 Idiom, 12 Earl, 13 Exam.

26

ACROSS: 1 Bobby socks, 5 Go halves, 9 Flip, 10 Olav, 11 Pagan, 12 Else, 14 Hart, 15 Kneehole, 18 Drop scones. DOWN: 1 Beefsteak, 2 Bagpipe, 3 Ova, 4 She, 6 Heigh-ho, 7 Val, 8 Seventies, 10 On the go, 13 Sue, 16 Nod, 17 Hop.

27

ACROSS: 1 Lace-trimmed, 5 Stashed, 9 Okra, 10 Orca, 11 Polyp, 12 Edge, 13 East, 14 Jet-wash, 16 Forced march. DOWN: 1 Lose oneself, 2 Cos, 3 Mud, 4 Drop a stitch, 6 Trapeze, 7 Swallow, 8 Elopers, 14 Jar, 15 Her.

28

ACROSS: 1 Brainpower, 7 Brood, 8 Intro, 9 Letting drop, 11 Juicy morsel, 14 Total, 15 Siren, 16 Bridgeable. DOWN: 1 Bubble-jets, 2 Aloft, 3 Nod, 4 Owing to, 5 Ester, 6 Corpulence, 10 Ivy-clad, 12 Inter, 13 Shrub, 15 See.

29

ACROSS: 1 Jubilee clip, 5 Caustic, 8 Eases, 9 Mambo, 10 Nadia, 12 Onset, 14 Prepare, 15 Schoolgirls. DOWN: 1 Juggernauts, 2 Bucks, 3 Locum, 4 Proportions, 6 Upstate, 7 Tombola, 11 Depth, 13 Swear.

30

ACROSS: 1 Lambasted, 5 Boa, 6 Sum, 7 Offer up, 10 Kit, 11 Invalid, 12 Ion, 13 Keen eye, 16 Mat, 17 Wan, 18 Gear ratio. DOWN: 1 Last time, 2 Memo, 3 Shoe, 4 Dropping in, 5 Bookmaking, 8 Flaky, 9 Radio Two, 14 Near, 15 Emit.

31

ACROSS: 1 Iron-hearted, 5 Petri, 7 Sepia, 9 Potomac, 11 Son,
12 Car, 13 Ontario, 16 Users, 17 Among, 18 Sea captains.
DOWN: 1 Impulse buys, 2 Hoist, 3 Assam, 4 Drawbridges,
6 Top note, 8 Piccolo, 10 Ova, 14 Testa, 15 Roast.

32

ACROSS: 1 Comforting, 7 Rinse, 8 Wigwams, 11 Drams, 13 Tiara,
14 Rissole, 16 Addle, 18 Lamprey eel. DOWN: 2 Own, 3 Flew solo,
4 Thaw, 5 Glasspaper, 6 Bridge roll, 9 Go steady, 10 Area, 12 Axis,
15 Snip, 17 Die.

33

ACROSS: 1 A little bird, 5 Non-stop, 8 Uncut, 9 Kylie, 10 Crust,
12 Nulls, 14 Tidings, 15 Emasculates. DOWN: 1 Acupuncture,
2 Ionic, 3 Impel, 4 Dealerships, 6 Notated, 7 Taken on, 11 Ultra,
13 Liszt.

34

ACROSS: 1 Bully beef, 5 DNA, 6 Sum, 7 Bull-bar, 10 Tar,
11 About to, 12 Ton, 13 She-wolf, 16 Lea, 17 Lad, 18 Downgrade.
DOWN: 1 Base rate, 2 Limb, 3 Bull, 4 Fair-minded, 5 Distressed,
8 Usual, 9 Boot sale, 14 Wean, 15 Flea.

35

ACROSS: 1 Bare midriff, 5 Desktop, 7 Again, 8 Olive, 9 Sinus,
11 Titan, 12 Prior to, 13 Marchioness. DOWN: 1 Big bass drum,
2 Mason, 3 Ditto, 4 Fingernails, 5 Drawn up, 6 Point to, 10 Smith,
11 Torso.

36

ACROSS: 1 Mount Sinai, 5 Grapples, 9 Path, 10 Calf, 11 Llano,
12 Navy, 14 Rove, 15 Kuwaitis, 18 Eavesdrops. DOWN: 1 Max
Planck, 2 Nightly, 3 Imp, 4 Ire, 6 Assault, 7 Lea, 8 Safe seats,
10 Coarser, 13 Vow, 16 Use, 17 Ice.

37

ACROSS: 1 Out for a duck, 5 Atomise, 9 Hair, 10 Heap, 11 Pablo, 12 Same, 13 Lion, 14 Nowhere, 16 Falls back on. DOWN: 1 Off the shelf, 2 Tea, 3 Ure, 4 King Penguin, 6 Torpedo, 7 Macbeth, 8 Scholar, 14 Nil, 15 Elk.

38

ACROSS: 1 Distribute, 6 Upon, 7 Ado, 8 Chef, 9 Fuel tank, 11 Forelegs, 14 Pong, 15 Red, 16 Aura, 17 Bon appetit. DOWN: 1 Discomfort, 2 Truffle, 3 Banal, 4 Tiara, 5 Forking out, 10 To spare, 12 Rodeo, 13 Llama.

39

ACROSS: 1 Curtain rail, 5 Bib, 7 Lea, 8 About to, 10 Bog down, 11 Recruit, 14 Thy, 15 Era, 16 Holy Trinity. DOWN: 1 Cable stitch, 2 Auto, 3 Newt, 4 Leading lady, 6 Banbury, 7 Low note, 9 Under, 12 Cast, 13 Ugli.

40

ACROSS: 1 Santa Claus, 5 Acrostic, 9 Told, 10 Soul, 11 Croci, 12 Rate, 14 Kind, 15 Zipporah, 18 Production. DOWN: 1 Santa Cruz, 2 Traduce, 3 Leo, 4 Ski, 6 Recover, 7 Too, 8 Calms down, 10 Silk hat, 13 Tap, 16 Imp, 17 Odd.

41

ACROSS: 1 Accelerated, 5 Off form, 9 Fear, 10 Stem, 11 Vague, 12 Redo, 13 Tuba, 14 Trinket, 16 Goes for gold. DOWN: 1 Acid-forming, 2 Coo, 3 Tam, 4 Disembarked, 6 Fervour, 7 Frogman, 8 Rosette, 14 Tie, 15 Two.

42

ACROSS: 1 Credential, 7 Manse, 8 Chino, 9 A bit of fluff, 11 I'll be blowed, 14 Euros, 15 Elfin, 16 Damp course. DOWN: 1 Campaniles, 2 Ennui, 3 Eve, 4 Tactful, 5 Adieu, 6 Confidence, 10 Opens up, 12 Larva, 13 Wafer, 15 Ego.

43

ACROSS: 1 Leading rein, 5 Dipoles, 8 Needs, 9 Thyme, 10 Quite, 12 Radii, 14 Earplug, 15 Holiday mood. DOWN: 1 Lemon squash, 2 Addle, 3 Essay, 4 Noble-minded, 6 Pasteur, 7 Literal, 11 Ideal, 13 Doggo.

44

ACROSS: 1 Fatty acid, 5 Coo, 6 Ohm, 7 Big idea, 10 Nun, 11 Open day, 12 Led, 13 Scenery, 16 Egg, 17 Hen, 18 Face paint. DOWN: 1 Footnote, 2 Tomb, 3 Anti, 4 Decahedron, 5 Cannons off, 8 Inner, 9 Daylight, 14 Nave, 15 Yeti.

45

ACROSS: 1 Move forward, 5 Drove, 7 Debug, 9 Largest, 11 Eli, 12 Sin, 13 Quantum, 16 Reeks, 17 Rinse, 18 Higher wages. DOWN: 1 Middle Earth, 2 Freer, 3 Ridge, 4 Dog fanciers, 6 Oblique, 8 Batsman, 10 Gin, 14 Aisle, 15 Throw.

46

ACROSS: 1 Barley wine, 7 Range, 8 Sub rosa, 11 Heart, 13 Totem, 14 Impalas, 16 He-man, 18 Candlewick. DOWN: 2 Awn, 3 Lie still, 4 Weir, 5 Embankment, 6 Arch critic, 9 Boat show, 10 Omit, 12 Atop, 15 Abed, 17 Mac.

47

ACROSS: 1 Long stretch, 5 Rises up, 8 Niece, 9 Endue, 10 Odour, 12 Remit, 14 Tick off, 15 Deoxidation. DOWN: 1 Learn to read, 2 Nurse, 3 Tepid, 4 Harvest moon, 6 Stearic, 7 Swear to, 11 Outdo, 13 Mufti.

48

ACROSS: 1 Assaulted, 5 Cur, 6 Red, 7 Sofa bed, 10 Its, 11 Too fast, 12 Ten, 13 Tadpole, 16 Woe, 17 Owl, 18 Presses on. DOWN: 1 Arrested, 2 Suds, 3 Lava, 4 Disdainful, 5 Comic strip, 8 Offal, 9 Battle on, 14 Plus, 15 Ewes.

49

ACROSS: 1 Handwriting, 5 Jump off, 7 Pumas, 8 Spike, 9 Irish, 11 Magic, 12 Rip-offs, 13 Deodorizers. DOWN: 1 Hand-painted, 2 Wombs, 3 Icons, 4 Golden curls, 5 Jumpier, 6 Fridges, 10 Hippo, 11 Mufti.

50

ACROSS: 1 Cantaloupe, 5 Addendum, 9 Roam, 10 Styx, 11 Latch, 12 Acme, 14 Tell, 15 Doorstep, 18 Bonesetter. DOWN: 1 Court card, 2 Trample, 3 Ode, 4 Emu, 6 Distort, 7 Dot, 8 Max Miller, 10 Shot put, 13 Moo, 16 Orb, 17 Sue.

51

ACROSS: 1 Oriel window, 5 Edibles, 9 Axis, 10 Atop, 11 Tramp, 12 Dodo, 13 Slot, 14 Attends, 16 Recognition. DOWN: 1 Over and over, 2 Ire, 3 Des, 4 Wave pattern, 6 Distort, 7 Because, 8 Elapsed, 14 Arc, 15 Ski.

52

ACROSS: 1 Brainstorm, 6 Vale, 7 Moo, 8 Visa, 9 Constant, 11 Antonyms, 14 Chat, 15 Tan, 16 Diva, 17 Breaks even. DOWN: 1 Bon vivants, 2 In vacuo, 3 Tress, 4 Rumba, 5 Bolt-action, 10 To scale, 12 Tenor, 13 Nadia.

53

ACROSS: 1 Cocktail bar, 5 Eat, 7 RNA, 8 Embrace, 10 Up and up, 11 Lying in, 14 Ova, 15 Don, 16 Feeler gauge. DOWN: 1 Creaming off, 2 Tomb, 3 Iota, 4 Reassurance, 6 Tequila, 7 Respond, 9 Run-in, 12 Idle, 13 Gong.

54

ACROSS: 1 King's Cross, 5 Expenses, 9 Know, 10 Nato, 11 Inure, 12 Oyez, 14 Diva, 15 Feel safe, 18 Regardless. DOWN: 1 Kicked off, 2 Gee whiz, 3 Rye, 4 She, 6 Petunia, 7 Spa, 8 Slope arms, 10 New Deal, 13 Ewe, 16 Err, 17 Sea.

55

ACROSS: 1 Cock and bull, 5 Brusque, 9 Item, 10 Anon,
11 Apron, 12 Iron, 13 Dash, 14 Pan pipe, 16 Large income.
DOWN: 1 Conditional, 2 Cab, 3 Use, 4 Lemon cheese, 6 Romania,
7 Shore up, 8 Up and up, 14 Par, 15 Ego.

56

ACROSS: 1 Dalton's law, 7 Image, 8 Undue, 9 Leading up to,
11 Over the moon, 14 Pin on, 15 Khaki, 16 Side by side.
DOWN: 1 Drill corps, 2 Llama, 3 Owe, 4 Smuggle, 5 Add up,
6 Aero engine, 10 Intense, 12 Ennui, 13 Omani, 15 Key.

57

ACROSS: 1 Motherboard, 5 Massage, 8 Thorn, 9 Ousel, 10 Issue,
12 Eases, 14 Awesome, 15 Hold in check. DOWN: 1 Mountain ash,
2 Tempo, 3 Avers, 4 Doubles back, 6 Sincere, 7 At one go,
11 Shawl, 13 Sieve.

58

ACROSS: 1 Au naturel, 5 Cur, 6 Caw, 7 Sleight, 10 Law,
11 Antenna, 12 Rut, 13 Misdeed, 16 Rod, 17 Urn, 18 Drawing up.
DOWN: 1 Archways, 2 News, 3 Ugli, 4 Last autumn, 5 Call to
mind, 8 Liege, 9 Geared up, 14 Draw, 15 Drag.

59

ACROSS: 1 Pole-vaulted, 5 Reign, 7 India, 9 Silesia, 11 Imp,
12 Wee, 13 In rough, 16 Breed, 17 Theta, 18 Examination.
DOWN: 1 Perceivable, 2 Vinyl, 3 Units, 4 Dead certain, 6 Inspire,
8 Draw hoe, 10 Ego, 14 Radii, 15 Ultra.

60

ACROSS: 1 Rabbit foot, 7 Ionic, 8 Tactile, 11 Tease, 13 Genii,
14 Impeach, 16 Tinge, 18 Tight spots. DOWN: 2 Awn, 3 Bacteria,
4 Fiat, 5 Typewriter, 6 Birthright, 9 Caught up, 10 Icon, 12 Atop,
15 Etch, 17 Net.

61

ACROSS: 1 Constructed, 5 Crackle, 8 Kirov, 9 Renal, 10 Nulls, 12 Cocos, 14 Martini, 15 Exhaustible. DOWN: 1 Chicken wire, 2 Nicer, 3 Tie in, 4 Double space, 6 Adviser, 7 Karachi, 11 Lymph, 13 Climb.

62

ACROSS: 1 Full board, 5 Boa, 6 Sea, 7 Pension, 10 Orb, 11 Upgrade, 12 Spa, 13 Jakarta, 16 Era, 17 The, 18 Existence. DOWN: 1 Fast buck, 2 Leap, 3 Odds, 4 Danny La Rue, 5 Bit of a joke, 8 Egret, 9 Ice skate, 14 Alms, 15 Aeon.

63

ACROSS: 1 Negative ion, 5 In a flap, 7 Op art, 8 Radio, 9 Adult, 11 Adorn, 12 Hat rack, 13 Circle dance. DOWN: 1 New Romantic, 2 Trait, 3 Velar, 4 Newborn babe, 5 In a rush, 6 Paddock, 10 Total, 11 Award.

64

ACROSS: 1 Tailing off, 5 Flaubert, 9 Pact, 10 Nova, 11 Evoke, 12 Opus, 14 Rule, 15 Fair wage, 18 Encounters. DOWN: 1 Tipped off, 2 Lefties, 3 Gnu, 4 Fur, 6 Antonia, 7 Ego, 8 Tea breaks, 10 Nearest, 13 Uri, 16 Aye, 17 Woo.

65

ACROSS: 1 Non-magnetic, 5 Laid low, 9 Open, 10 Okra, 11 Ester, 12 Ours, 13 Dale, 14 Rangers, 16 Roman Empire. DOWN: 1 Not go too far, 2 Nil, 3 Tow, 4 Cock-a-leekie, 6 Amnesia, 7 Dieting, 8 On order, 14 Rim, 15 Ski.

66

ACROSS: 1 Backhander, 6 Numb, 7 Sir, 8 Kilt, 9 Incenses, 11 Deciding, 14 Hula, 15 Wee, 16 Tent, 17 Go to pieces. DOWN: 1 Backed down, 2 Kon-Tiki, 3 Noble, 4 Eases, 5 Cross hairs, 10 Nightie, 12 Credo, 13 Ditto.

67

ACROSS: 1 Scout around, 5 Irk, 7 Few, 8 Egg roll, 10 Pigment, 11 Earache, 14 But, 15 Rot, 16 Leaderboard. DOWN: 1 Sticky label, 2 Tang, 3 Redo, 4 Downhearted, 6 Keepnet, 7 Flatter, 9 Rumba, 12 Race, 13 Curb.

68

ACROSS: 1 Daily round, 5 Gold disc, 9 Magi, 10 Pyre, 11 Lasso, 12 Lose, 14 Etch, 15 Swings by, 18 Breaks down. DOWN: 1 Drum rolls, 2 Legible, 3 Old, 4 Do's, 6 Lessons, 7 Icy, 8 Cream horn, 10 Pop-eyed, 13 Ski, 16 Web, 17 Goa.

69

ACROSS: 1 New Year's Eve, 5 Stubble, 9 Idea, 10 Mesh, 11 Champ, 12 Bush, 13 Solo, 14 Satsuma, 16 Form teacher. DOWN: 1 News in brief, 2 Was, 3 Eve, 4 Earth mother, 6 Trachea, 7 Bewails, 8 Lump sum, 14 Sir, 15 Ash.

70

ACROSS: 1 Bottleneck, 7 Lobby, 8 Tempi, 9 Troublesome, 11 Intense cold, 14 Opera, 15 Medic, 16 Deferments. DOWN: 1 B flat minor, 2 Taboo, 3 Lay, 4 Not here, 5 Cameo, 6 Eider ducks, 10 Bandage, 12 There, 13 Olden, 15 Mum.

71

ACROSS: 1 Nessun Dorma, 5 Rippled, 8 Robot, 9 Worst, 10 Tyson, 12 Infer, 14 Up ahead, 15 Life is sweet. DOWN: 1 Nature trail, 2 Shrub, 3 Radar, 4 All-star cast, 6 Petunia, 7 Low tide, 11 Snuff, 13 Fudge.

72

ACROSS: 1 Doglegged, 5 Duo, 6 Tom, 7 Stand-up, 10 Huh, 11 Eclipse, 12 Ski, 13 Gas jets, 16 Tow, 17 Ash, 18 Flies away. DOWN: 1 Dot the i's, 2 Gums, 3 Gown, 4 Drop stitch, 5 Dashing off, 8 Twist, 9 Dies away, 14 Jade, 15 Stew.

73

ACROSS: 1 Centenarian, 5 Opted, 7 Admit, 9 Low beam,
11 Ere, 12 Men, 13 Nairobi, 16 Aisle, 17 Assai, 18 Large whisky.
DOWN: 1 Croquet ball, 2 Endow, 3 Awake, 4 Nationality,
6 Talents, 8 Mummies, 10 Bar, 14 Irene, 15 Orach.

74

ACROSS: 1 Eyeballing, 7 Pasta, 8 Bye-byes, 11 Rebus, 13 Stoic,
14 Cheetah, 16 Enact, 18 Distillers. DOWN: 2 Yes, 3 Be absent,
4 Limb, 5 Goes back to, 6 Approached, 9 Eggshell, 10 Yo-yo,
12 Bade, 15 Exit, 17 Air.

75

ACROSS: 1 Nature lover, 5 Rotates, 8 Lie-in, 9 Outdo, 10 Cover,
12 Piano, 14 Samurai, 15 Large amount. DOWN: 1 Naval school,
2 Throe, 3 Visit, 4 Retrorocket, 6 Tantrum, 7 Trooper, 11 Visor,
13 Adieu.

76

ACROSS: 1 Arc welded, 5 Dip, 6 PPS, 7 Heigh-ho!, 10 Ore,
11 Pachisi, 12 Rut, 13 Cue card, 16 Eli, 17 Nee, 18 Gift horse.
DOWN: 1 Apple pie, 2 Cash, 3 Lung, 4 Dr Dolittle, 5 Denouncing,
8 Ether, 9 Hairline, 14 Clot, 15 Dear.

77

ACROSS: 1 Matchmaking, 5 Hearing, 7 Famed, 8 Moors, 9 Equip,
11 Denim, 12 Going up, 13 Hold on tight. DOWN: 1 Man of wealth,
2 Hoard, 3 Axiom, 4 Gross amount, 5 Hamburg, 6 Grown-up,
10 Primo, 11 Digit.

78

ACROSS: 1 Disposable, 5 Cupcakes, 9 Neat, 10 Atom, 11 Recap,
12 Idle, 14 Lour, 15 Shoebill, 18 Catalysers. DOWN: 1 Dawn raids,
2 Picture, 3 Arc, 4 Ewe, 6 Puccini, 7 Kit, 8 Summaries, 10 Apollos,
13 Leo, 16 Hic, 17 Boa.

79

ACROSS: 1 Name-calling, 5 Malaise, 9 Abet, 10 Edge, 11 Epoch, 12 Damn, 13 Ecru, 14 Palaver, 16 Loses weight. DOWN: 1 Nice and cool, 2 Mum, 3 Ire, 4 Glove puppet, 6 Antenna, 7 Antonia, 8 See here, 14 PPS, 15 Rig.

80

ACROSS: 1 First steps, 6 Abet, 7 Ova, 8 Evil, 9 Eclipsed, 11 Eyepiece, 14 Bell, 15 Cut, 16 Area, 17 Camcorders. DOWN: 1 Free French, 2 Scale up, 3 Tutti, 4 Proms, 5 Candyfloss, 10 Piebald, 12 Extra, 13 Isaac.

81

ACROSS: 1 Not counting, 5 Via, 7 BMA, 8 No reply, 10 Tribune, 11 Moodier, 14 Ice, 15 Tit, 16 Glossed over. DOWN: 1 Naval rating, 2 Over, 3 Neap, 4 Grave matter, 6 Anytime, 7 By heart, 9 Embed, 12 Onus, 13 Ibid.

82

ACROSS: 1 Waste paper, 5 Tails off, 9 Ajar, 10 Heir, 11 Tiara, 12 Idle, 14 Ludo, 15 Realises, 18 Falls apart. DOWN: 1 Wigan Pier, 2 Titrate, 3 Ail, 4 RAF, 6 In pairs, 7 Ode, 8 Forecourt, 10 Hauls up, 13 Lea, 16 Elf, 17 III.

83

ACROSS: 1 Non-stick pan, 5 Tenfold, 9 Czar, 10 Veto, 11 Agree, 12 Dent, 13 Aria, 14 Scuttle, 16 Land reforms. DOWN: 1 No pack drill, 2 Not, 3 Pod, 4 New potatoes, 6 Erratic, 7 Fairest, 8 Love all, 14 Sun, 15 Err.

84

ACROSS: 1 Free access, 7 Rover, 8 Earth, 9 Insuperable, 11 Intersperse, 14 Rhyme, 15 Comma, 16 Centigrade. DOWN: 1 Fortifiers, 2 Elves, 3 Air, 4 Cheer up, 5 Scrub, 6 Cheesecake, 10 Portent, 12 Thyme, 13 Rumba, 15 Cog.

85

ACROSS: 1 On account of, 5 Decapod, 8 Lingo, 9 Reset, 10 Tempt, 12 Nasal, 14 Juniper, 15 Spreadeagle. DOWN: 1 Open letters, 2 Add-on, 3 To-dos, 4 Frontal lobe, 6 Crouton, 7 Parsnip, 11 Major, 13 Sprig.

86

ACROSS: 1 Boycotted, 5 Eel, 6 Awl, 7 Payslip, 10 Ask, 11 Explain, 12 Oil, 13 Itemise, 16 Uri, 17 Lie, 18 Dress code. DOWN: 1 Black eye, 2 Yelp, 3 Thus, 4 Drops a line, 5 Empathized, 8 Atlas, 9 Lino tile, 14 Moss, 15 Euro.

87

ACROSS: 1 Oil painting, 5 Torso, 7 Sepia, 9 Awfully, 11 Tam, 12 Map, 13 In peace, 16 Ingot, 17 Actin, 18 Naval forces. DOWN: 1 Ostentation, 2 Aloof, 3 Nasal, 4 Gramophones, 6 Reaming, 8 Payment, 10 Use, 14 Petal, 15 Alamo.

88

ACROSS: 1 Boyfriends, 7 Rangy, 8 Softest, 11 Notch, 13 Recto, 14 Robotic, 16 Ounce, 18 Flamboyant. DOWN: 2 Own, 3 Fly sheet, 4 Edit, 5 South Korea, 6 French roof, 9 Fair copy, 10 Epic, 12 Tomb, 15 Ovum, 17 Nun.

89

ACROSS: 1 Ore smelting, 5 Playlet, 8 Crypt, 9 Eerie, 10 Adorn, 12 Adieu, 14 Sparkle, 15 Masterfully. DOWN: 1 Officialdom, 2 Empty, 3 Inter, 4 Guide pulley, 6 Antonia, 7 Lie back, 11 Oasis, 13 Ideal.

90

ACROSS: 1 Assembled, 5 For, 6 Too, 7 Tuneful, 10 Ups, 11 Tensing, 12 Hob, 13 Sockets, 16 Oaf, 17 Owl, 18 Cornflour. DOWN: 1 Artistic, 2 Shot, 3 Bode, 4 Dollar bill, 5 Futuristic, 8 Upset, 9 Fight for, 14 Kiln, 15 Solo.

91

ACROSS: 1 In a flat spin, 5 Rebuses, 7 Venal, 8 Ember, 9 Risks, 11 Prize, 12 Peerage, 13 The once over. DOWN: 1 Inadvertent, 2 Label, 3 Taste, 4 No surrender, 5 Rings up, 6 Subside, 10 Skein, 11 Phase.

92

ACROSS: 1 Degradable, 5 Carts off, 9 Inky, 10 Gang, 11 Local, 12 Rime, 14 Tomb, 15 Duty-free, 18 Alarm clock. DOWN: 1 Delivered, 2 Recycle, 3 Ant, 4 Elf, 6 Rancour, 7 Ova, 8 Fight back, 10 Gluteal, 13 Mat, 16 USA, 17 Fir.

93

ACROSS: 1 Molar weight, 5 Sparing, 9 Idol, 10 Wash, 11 Elena, 12 Earn, 13 Gain, 14 Gas fire, 16 Pot the black. DOWN: 1 Machine shop, 2 Lbs, 3 Gig, 4 Tony Hancock, 6 Polenta, 7 Rope off, 8 New Ager, 14 Get, 15 Era.

94

ACROSS: 1 Decorative, 6 Flip, 7 Coo, 8 Bali, 9 Chuckled, 11 Be around, 14 Nova, 15 Ski, 16 Acne, 17 Diminishes. DOWN: 1 Double bass, 2 Officer, 3 Topic, 4 Vocal, 5 Folded arms, 10 Kidneys, 12 Alibi, 13 Okapi.

95

ACROSS: 1 Nobel prizes, 5 Cog, 7 Rye, 8 Romania, 10 Melange, 11 Lens cap, 14 Eye, 15 Ski, 16 Stage-manage. DOWN: 1 Nice manners, 2 Loam, 3 Roan, 4 Steam engine, 6 Grumble, 7 Rave-ups, 9 Amass, 12 Node, 13 Coda.

96

ACROSS: 1 Extricated, 5 Cash flow, 9 Loci, 10 Taxi, 11 Swami, 12 Neat, 14 Oath, 15 Drops off, 18 Boiler suit. DOWN: 1 Explained, 2 Raciest, 3 Ash, 4 Duo, 6 Speak to, 7 Lea, 8 White Hart, 10 Tip-offs, 13 Ado, 16 Rob, 17 Sol.

97

ACROSS: 1 Mercury lamp, 5 Probate, 9 Iron, 10 Anti, 11 Dukes, 12 GIGO, 13 Take, 14 Answers, 16 Take on board. DOWN: 1 Mailing list, 2 Rip, 3 Age, 4 Pensive mood, 6 Ran down, 7 Back row, 8 Toaster, 14 Auk, 15 Spa.

98

ACROSS: 1 Deals a blow, 7 Aloha, 8 Otter, 9 Minor canons, 11 Remonstrate, 14 India, 15 Ennui, 16 Bank vaults. DOWN: 1 Dean Martin, 2 Adorn, 3 Sea, 4 Buoyant, 5 Outdo, 6 Brasseries, 10 Ransack, 12 Media, 13 Annul, 15 Era.

99

ACROSS: 1 Court jester, 5 Conifer, 8 Inter, 9 Rebut, 10 Limbo, 12 Imbue, 14 Last act, 15 Running knot. DOWN: 1 Cauliflower, 2 Uncut, 3 Throb, 4 Rock the boat, 6 Narrows, 7 Formica, 11 Melon, 13 Baton.

100

ACROSS: 1 Exceeding, 5 Gym, 6 Per, 7 Picador, 10 Era, 11 Stencil, 12 Lid, 13 In store, 16 Dud, 17 Urn, 18 Double top. DOWN: 1 Emphasis, 2 Carp, 3 Diva, 4 Geared down, 5 Greenfield, 8 Inner, 9 Dolled up, 14 Tomb, 15 Edit.

101

ACROSS: 1 Contraption, 5 At sea, 7 Aspen, 9 Nomadic, 11 Ass, 12 Has, 13 Puccini, 16 Often, 17 Alibi, 18 Replacement. DOWN: 1 Chain armour, 2 Realm, 3 Plaid, 4 Nondescript, 6 Sunspot, 8 Pachisi, 10 Arc, 14 Conga, 15 Image.

102

ACROSS: 1 Bad manners, 7 Olden, 8 Off-base, 11 Night, 13 Kebab, 14 Remorse, 16 Extol, 18 Expression. DOWN: 2 Aid, 3 Minotaur, 4 Numb, 5 Safety bolt, 6 Going price, 9 For keeps, 10 Arab, 12 Glum, 15 Over, 17 Too.

103

ACROSS: 1 Pink Panther, 5 Details, 8 Kayak, 9 Pearl, 10 Edwin, 12 Newts, 14 Linseed, 15 Scholarship. DOWN: 1 Park keepers, 2 Noddy, 3 Hosta, 4 Rumble strip, 6 Taken in, 7 Impinge, 11 Welsh, 13 Width.

104

ACROSS: 1 Insurance, 5 Gin, 6 Fur, 7 Farther, 10 DNA, 11 Tastier, 12 Mac, 13 Cassock, 16 New, 17 And, 18 Free entry. DOWN: 1 Inflates, 2 Surf, 3 Abet, 4 Entrenched, 5 Golden calf, 8 Attic, 9 Harm's way, 14 Save, 15 Knit.

105

ACROSS: 1 Carrot flies, 5 Bad omen, 7 Union, 8 Rotor, 9 Put-up, 11 Swain, 12 Naivety, 13 New York City. DOWN: 1 Consumption, 2 Olden, 3 Femur, 4 Solar energy, 5 Built-in, 6 Not many, 10 Primo, 11 Sneak.

106

ACROSS: 1 Bill of sale, 5 Anteroom, 9 Ugli, 10 Peru, 11 Occur, 12 Naan, 14 Diva, 15 Earpiece, 18 Carpenters. DOWN: 1 Beau monde, 2 Liaison, 3 See, 4 Ego, 6 Trickle, 7 Ode, 8 Mountains, 10 Prudent, 13 Air, 16 Arc, 17 Imp.

107

ACROSS: 1 Backstreets, 5 Thought, 9 Earn, 10 Ache, 11 Bored, 12 Okra, 13 Serf, 14 Receipt, 16 Naval battle. DOWN: 1 Barrel organ, 2 Cut, 3 Eat, 4 Slice of life, 6 Henbane, 7 Upgrade, 8 Heads-up, 14 Rev, 15 Tot.

108

ACROSS: 1 Gas cookers, 6 Rump, 7 Car, 8 Down, 9 Controls, 11 Airbrick, 14 Sofa, 15 Elm, 16 Posh, 17 Fall in with. DOWN: 1 Golden ages, 2 Corncob, 3 Kaput, 4 Recto, 5 Cross-hatch, 10 Rikshaw, 12 Rumba, 13 Repel.

9

CROSS: 1 Cod liver oil, 5 Ale, 7 Boo, 8 Rampage, 10 Spatula, 1 Notices, 14 Keg, 15 Err, 16 Running sore. DOWN: 1 Chain locker, 2 Item, 3 Etna, 4 Loomed large, 6 Erasing, 7 Because, 9 Petri, 12 Taxi, 13 Clog.

110

ACROSS: 1 Abatements, 5 Adjacent, 9 Ugli, 10 Taxi, 11 Saudi, 12 Isle, 14 Brat, 15 Egg white, 18 Buttermilk. DOWN: 1 About time, 2 Traipse, 3 Eva, 4 Sin, 6 Jacuzzi, 7 Era, 8 Think tank, 10 Tie beam, 13 Log, 16 Gab, 17 Hat.

111

ACROSS: 1 Nobody knows, 5 Suffuse, 9 Tang, 10 Talc, 11 Rapid, 12 Aura, 13 Okra, 14 Pending, 16 Go one better. DOWN: 1 Negotiating, 2 Bus, 3 Owe, 4 Safecracker, 6 Upgrade, 7 Flipped, 8 Sat down, 14 Pro, 15 Gut.

112

ACROSS: 1 Ginger cake, 7 Lathe, 8 Loans, 9 Millionaire, 11 Neutral axis, 14 Nadia, 15 Bongo, 16 Crossbones. DOWN: 1 Gold mining, 2 Natal, 3 Ere, 4 Colonel, 5 Khaki, 6 Aspersions, 10 Inroads, 12 Under, 13 Xenon, 15 Bib.

113

ACROSS: 1 Oft-repeated, 5 Siberia, 8 Idyll, 9 Sonic, 10 Abash, 12 Ditto, 14 Papayas, 15 Non-starters. DOWN: 1 Original sin, 2 Tasty, 3 Train, 4 Directories, 6 Bellhop, 7 Rest day, 11 Aspen, 13 Taste.

114

ACROSS: 1 Bad for one, 5 Air, 6 Err, 7 Kampala, 10 Oak, 11 Inveigh, 12 Tit, 13 Magnets, 16 Ova, 17 Yes, 18 Iron Cross. DOWN: 1 Breaking, 2 Dark, 3 Reap, 4 Escalators, 5 Anno Domini, 8 Agent, 9 Ashtrays, 14 Noon, 15 So-so.

115

ACROSS: 1 Indentation, 5 Yodel, 7 Onset, 9 Pink gin, 11 Rap, 12 Ki◼
13 Linnets, 16 Nadir, 17 Canoe, 18 Spaceflight. DOWN: 1 In your
hands, 2 Nylon, 3 Among, 4 Net interest, 6 Dappled, 8 Sinks in,
10 Ken, 14 Nurse, 15 Excel.

116

ACROSS: 1 Fobbing off, 7 Rebel, 8 Learner, 11 Awash, 13 Extra,
14 Drinker, 16 Ensue, 18 Foreground. DOWN: 2 Orb, 3 Billhook,
4 Gear, 5 Four-seater, 6 Creamed off, 9 Alter ego, 10 Nest,
12 Anti, 15 Nice, 17 Sin.

117

ACROSS: 1 Madder brown, 5 Defuses, 8 Theta, 9 Asset, 10 Taste,
12 Umbel, 14 In place, 15 Safety first. DOWN: 1 Move to tears,
2 Dodge, 3 Oasis, 4 Night flight, 6 Frame-up, 7 Spatula, 11 Skiff,
13 Blear.

118

ACROSS: 1 Abounding, 5 Gab, 6 Sod, 7 Spiraea, 10 Nun,
11 Tipster, 12 Cow, 13 Open day, 16 Ova, 17 Fad, 18 Appellant.
DOWN: 1 Absinthe, 2 Odds, 3 Dear, 4 Go backward, 5 Going to
sea, 8 Pasta, 9 Aircraft, 14 Nine, 15 Yoga.

119

ACROSS: 1 Information, 5 Inveigh, 7 Expel, 8 Mulch, 9 Skiff,
11 Pop-up, 12 Tenancy, 13 Needlecraft. DOWN: 1 Impress upon,
2 Rival, 3 Axiom, 4 Not the point, 5 Imprint, 6 Half-pay, 10 Final,
11 Panic.

120

ACROSS: 1 A high price, 5 Notebook, 9 Pond, 10 Idle,
11 Grimm, 12 Less, 14 Earn, 15 Armament, 18 Go for a spin.
DOWN: 1 A cappella, 2 Gundogs, 3 Roe, 4 Ego, 6 Trainee, 7 Old,
8 Keeping on, 10 Impetus, 13 Sum, 16 Rug, 17 Moo.

1

CROSS: 1 Petty-minded, 5 Protest, 9 Teal, 10 More, 11 Extra, 12 Ezra, 13 Taxi, 14 Menorca, 16 Legal rights. DOWN: 1 Play the fool, 2 Tip, 3 Dot, 4 Disbelieves, 6 Release, 7 Testudo, 8 Somatic, 14 Mug, 15 Ash.

122

ACROSS: 1 Father's Day, 6 Damp, 7 Ice, 8 Lair, 9 Abrasive, 11 A bientot, 14 Buff, 15 Nil, 16 Viva, 17 Go fly a kite. DOWN: 1 Feels faint, 2 Hydrate, 3 Sepia, 4 Alibi, 5 Heretofore, 10 Sit back, 12 Igloo, 13 Naval.

123

ACROSS: 1 Pressed down, 5 Lap, 7 Sob, 8 In-group, 10 Matinee, 11 Not nice, 14 Oat, 15 Ski, 16 News summary. DOWN: 1 Pulling down, 2 Slag, 3 Dodo, 4 Noble family, 6 Pigment, 7 Spheres, 9 Reign, 12 Togs, 13 Item.

124

ACROSS: 1 Absolutely, 5 Long gone, 9 Yell, 10 Kelp, 11 Melee, 12 Trap, 14 Pupa, 15 Hotlines, 18 Five senses. DOWN: 1 Away match, 2 Oil lamp, 3 Tag, 4 Yen, 6 Nail gun, 7 Owe, 8 Euphrates, 10 Keeps on, 13 Aft, 16 Oaf, 17 Ice.

125

ACROSS: 1 Camel driver, 5 Titmice, 9 Knit, 10 Wane, 11 Ruing, 12 Thou, 13 Iris, 14 Retails, 16 Love is blind. DOWN: 1 Cricket ball, 2 Mat, 3 Vie, 4 Rhode Island, 6 Intrude, 7 Marimba, 8 Cowgirl, 14 Rev, 15 Ski.

126

ACROSS: 1 Hand lotion, 7 Gully, 8 Primo, 9 Fanatically, 11 Iconoclasts, 14 Rhoda, 15 Arena, 16 Heat shield. DOWN: 1 High-fliers, 2 Nylon, 3 Lay, 4 Topical, 5 Oriel, 6 Holy Island, 10 Too fast, 12 Ozone, 13 Swede, 15 Ash.

127

ACROSS: 1 Counterfoil, 5 Tatting, 8 Ogres, 9 Vital, 10 Sofia, 12 Llama, 14 Upended, 15 Leg of mutton. DOWN: 1 Carbon steel, 2 Utter, 3 Ought, 4 Legal jargon, 6 To spare, 7 Invalid, 11 Flung, 13 Audit.

128

ACROSS: 1 Guy Fawkes, 5 Fro, 6 Inn, 7 Stand to, 10 Egg, 11 Bullace, 12 Dub, 13 Indians, 16 Ova, 17 Cut, 18 Horseback. DOWN: 1 Going bad, 2 Yens, 3 Worn, 4 Second best, 5 Fever pitch, 8 Talon, 9 Died back, 14 Iris, 15 Soda.

129

ACROSS: 1 Chrome steel, 5 Onset, 7 Kirov, 9 Refusal, 11 Rio, 12 Len, 13 Chassis, 16 Short, 17 Ennui, 18 Safe conduct. DOWN: 1 Crown roasts, 2 Motif, 3 Sikhs, 4 Love-in-a-mist, 6 Sirocco, 8 Rolls in, 10 Ups, 14 Antic, 15 Stern.

130

ACROSS: 1 Column inch, 7 Isles, 8 Toasted, 11 Alibi, 13 Extra, 14 Clauses, 16 Inert, 18 Endowments. DOWN: 2 Oil, 3 Up sticks, 4 Ibis, 5 Head starts, 6 Final scene, 9 Adhesive, 10 Taut, 12 Idea, 15 Undo, 17 Eat.

131

ACROSS: 1 Home address, 5 Nibbles, 8 Ousel, 9 Greet, 10 Lusty, 12 Tilth, 14 Rapiers, 15 Nowhere to go. DOWN: 1 Haemoglobin, 2 Manes, 3 Ensue, 4 Stretch limo, 6 Belly up, 7 Legatee, 11 Shrew, 13 Lasso.

132

ACROSS: 1 Freestyle, 5 Goa, 6 Ice, 7 Dentate, 10 Nod, 11 Eloping, 12 RNA, 13 Holdall, 16 Out, 17 Icy, 18 Prise open. DOWN: 1 Fair deal, 2 Eyed, 3 Test, 4 Expectancy, 5 Going cheap, 8 Expel, 9 Au gratin, 14 Dais, 15 Loop.

133

ACROSS: 1 Proposition, 5 Off-beam, 7 Infer, 8 Lingo, 9 Grass, 11 Kirov, 12 Stencil, 13 Ringmasters. DOWN: 1 Pulling over, 2 Offer, 3 Ideal, 4 Narrow views, 5 Off days, 6 Mandrel, 10 Steam, 11 Kicks.

134

ACROSS: 1 Astronauts, 5 Go to jail, 9 Tosh, 10 Bloc, 11 Extra, 12 Lied, 14 Kilo, 15 At dinner, 18 Boil down to. DOWN: 1 Australia, 2 Righted, 3 Ago, 4 Ski, 6 Tuition, 7 Awl, 8 Locks onto, 10 Back row, 13 End, 16 Tab, 17 Nil.

135

ACROSS: 1 Paediatrics, 5 Thrifty, 9 News, 10 Czar, 11 Boric, 12 Rune, 13 Anew, 14 Initial, 16 Pulling back. DOWN: 1 Partnership, 2 Eat, 3 Icy, 4 Sparrowhawk, 6 Has-been, 7 In trust, 8 Toccata, 14 Ill, 15 Lea.

136

ACROSS: 1 First issue, 6 Memo, 7 Doe, 8 Taxi, 9 Tax forms, 11 Peaceful, 14 Suds, 15 Nag, 16 Talk, 17 Breaking up. DOWN: 1 Fly-tipping, 2 Semitic, 3 Scoff, 4 Udder, 5 Censorship, 10 Oilskin, 12 Augur, 13 Extra.

137

ACROSS: 1 Penny bazaar, 5 Was, 7 Uri, 8 Kinship, 10 Tunisia, 11 Holy One, 14 Icy, 15 Ski, 16 Sandown Park. DOWN: 1 Powertrains, 2 Yarn, 3 Arch, 4 Raise a stink, 6 Sketchy, 7 Updates, 9 Shiny, 12 Lego, 13 Omen.

138

ACROSS: 1 All set to go, 5 Improved, 9 Even, 10 Beta, 11 Amble, 12 Boyd, 14 Ugli, 15 Crumbles, 18 Despondent. DOWN: 1 Anaerobic, 2 Shinpad, 3 Tar, 4 One, 6 Parboil, 7 Vie, 8 Dead right, 10 Bemused, 13 You, 16 Rid, 17 Bap.

139

ACROSS: 1 Crestfallen, 5 Ticking, 9 Into, 10 Tare, 11 Niece, 12 Ella,
13 Airy, 14 Defrays, 16 Leeds United. DOWN: 1 Continental, 2 Eat,
3 Log, 4 Nurserymaid, 6 Iron age, 7 Kneeler, 8 Not easy, 14 Die,
15 Set.

140

ACROSS: 1 Dorchester, 7 Nylon, 8 Awash, 9 Racecourses,
11 Archdeacons, 14 Drill, 15 Piano, 16 Garden City.
DOWN: 1 Donor cards, 2 Relic, 3 Hen, 4 Scapula, 5 Exams,
6 Ghost story, 10 Coddled, 12 China, 13 Okapi, 15 Pen.

141

ACROSS: 1 Catch the ear, 5 Up to par, 8 Mayan, 9 Cheer, 10 Layer,
12 Samba, 14 Call off, 15 No admission. DOWN: 1 Cool million,
2 Truly, 3 Eerie, 4 Reformation, 6 Tendril, 7 Picasso, 11 Yucca,
13 Mufti.

142

ACROSS: 1 Pegged out, 5 Goa, 6 Tow, 7 Put back, 10 Née,
11 Relabel, 12 Rut, 13 Assizes, 16 Emu, 17 NME, 18 Aforesaid.
DOWN: 1 Patterns, 2 Gawp, 3 Daub, 4 Ticker tape, 5 Giant panda,
8 Usage, 9 All-round, 14 Ivor, 15 Sera.

143

ACROSS: 1 Radiator cap, 5 Accra, 7 Eager, 9 Montana,
11 Sue, 12 Sol, 13 Numbers, 16 Eased, 17 Hosed, 18 Hearty cheer.
DOWN: 1 Read a speech, 2 Again, 3 Opera, 4 Party leader,
6 Cements, 8 Glasses, 10 Tub, 14 Midst, 15 Ethic.

144

ACROSS: 1 Human being, 7 Irish, 8 Ensured, 11 Motor, 13 Corps,
14 Log book, 16 Sepia, 18 Field sport. DOWN: 2 Uri, 3 Adhere to,
4 Ecru, 5 Garden seat, 6 Firm belief, 9 Stacks up, 10 Roar,
12 Tang, 15 Bail, 17 Per.

ROSS: 1 Importation, 5 Rub it in, 8 Crest, 9 CD-ROM, 10 Untie, Laser, 14 Tunisia, 15 None so blind. DOWN: 1 In seclusion, 2 Puree, 3 Inner, 4 New improved, 6 Bittern, 7 Tickles, 11 Titan, 13 Swami.

146

ACROSS: 1 Regarding, 5 Fee, 6 PPS, 7 Peoples, 10 Sea, 11 Tending, 12 Tar, 13 Maddens, 16 Orb, 17 Lie, 18 Overvalue. DOWN: 1 Repeated, 2 Gasp, 3 Deep, 4 Ghost write, 5 Fats Domino, 8 End-on, 9 Log table, 14 Deer, 15 Soul.

147

ACROSS: 1 Herd of goats, 5 Sets off, 7 Stain, 8 Layer, 9 Havoc, 11 Bowel, 12 Summary, 13 Spoiled brat. DOWN: 1 High schools, 2 Often, 3 Ghoul, 4 Self-reliant, 5 Scarves, 6 Fly-away, 10 Camel, 11 Board.

148

ACROSS: 1 Apple sauce, 5 Bathrobe, 9 Also, 10 Ramp, 11 Rupee, 12 Toss, 14 Nuts, 15 Catsuits, 18 Decolonise. DOWN: 1 Antarctic, 2 Labours, 3 Ash, 4 Ebb, 6 Tripoli, 7 Ova, 8 Expensive, 10 Reins in, 13 Sot, 16 Aid, 17 UFO.

149

ACROSS: 1 Claw hammers, 5 Scrumpy, 9 Gown, 10 Mood, 11 Tramp, 12 Dido, 13 Kilo, 14 Propane, 16 Nation-state. DOWN: 1 Changed down, 2 Ass, 3 Ely, 4 Salad course, 6 Contour, 7 UEFA Cup, 8 Pumpkin, 14 Pat, 15 Era.

150

ACROSS: 1 Flash lamps, 6 Anti, 7 USA, 8 Lair, 9 Come upon, 11 Hog roast, 14 Hula, 15 Pin, 16 Tire, 17 Giro cheque. DOWN: 1 Full of hope, 2 Scarcer, 3 Alive, 4 Plump, 5 Bains-marie, 10 Up there, 12 Genii, 13 Outdo.

151

ACROSS: 1 Steals a kiss, 5 Rut, 7 Fie, 8 Offline, 10 Lessons,
11 Invoice, 14 Vat, 15 Dye, 16 Literary man. DOWN: 1 Street level,
2 Loaf, 3 Anti, 4 Stem to stern, 6 Toolkit, 7 Feasted, 9 Lasso,
12 Veer, 13 Ivor.

152

ACROSS: 1 Arbitrator, 5 Anaconda, 9 Oath, 10 Drip, 11 Liege,
12 Tube, 14 Igor, 15 Cartland, 18 Heat rashes. DOWN: 1 Acrobatic,
2 In a hole, 3 Arc, 4 Rid, 6 Almeria, 7 Nor, 8 Alpha rays,
10 Decides, 13 Bar, 16 Ash, 17 Lot.

153

ACROSS: 1 Portmanteau, 5 Triceps, 9 Loan, 10 Tear, 11 Cacti,
12 GIGO, 13 Fear, 14 Tripoli, 16 Stock market. DOWN: 1 Pearly
gates, 2 Rat, 3 E.g.s, 4 Under arrest, 6 Rancour, 7 Catch up,
8 Pitiful, 14 Too, 15 Ilk.

154

ACROSS: 1 Fearful din, 7 Raise, 8 Scuba, 9 Raising hell,
11 Net receipts, 14 Ennui, 15 Geese, 16 Brandysnap.
DOWN: 1 Forerunner, 2 Alibi, 3 Fie, 4 Lasagne, 5 Inure,
6 Fall asleep, 10 Iberian, 12 Tenor, 13 Preen, 15 Guy.

155

ACROSS: 1 Snowy orchid, 5 Rod Hull, 8 Lasso, 9 Proof, 10 Ice up,
12 Angel, 14 Radiate, 15 Street lamps. DOWN: 1 Scilly Isles,
2 Ogres, 3 Hello, 4 Dutifulness, 6 Dropped, 7 Uppsala, 11 Error,
13 Gleam.

156

ACROSS: 1 All is well, 5 Flu, 6 The, 7 Skulked, 10 Tam,
11 Newbury, 12 Pps, 13 Colombo, 16 Ski, 17 Nip, 18 First coat.
DOWN: 1 Autumnal, 2 Lees, 3 Well, 4 Leadership, 5 Fatted calf,
8 Kebab, 9 Key point, 14 Opus, 15 Oslo.

157

ACROSS: 1 Paraphrases, 5 Lemon, 7 Newel, 9 Clashed,
11 Use, 12 Ely, 13 Oakland, 16 Hello, 17 Tenet, 18 Sidestreets.
DOWN: 1 Pull punches, 2 Panda, 3 Ranch, 4 Sell by dates,
6 Mace oil, 8 Waded in, 10 Sol, 14 Knows, 15 After.

158

ACROSS: 1 Commenting, 7 Rebus, 8 Quarter, 11 Nehru, 13 Input,
14 Lincoln, 16 Grave, 18 Force apart. DOWN: 2 Orb, 3 Mosquito,
4 Tour, 5 Guarantees, 6 French loaf, 9 Adding up, 10 Trip, 12 Horn,
15 Chic, 17 Air.

159

ACROSS: 1 Open cheques, 5 Washtub, 8 Ounce, 9 Pin-up,
10 Recap, 12 Irked, 14 Pledged, 15 Deerstalker. DOWN: 1 Off your
head, 2 Edwin, 3 Urban, 4 Stopped over, 6 Steeple, 7 Topping,
11 Copse, 13 Kodak.

160

ACROSS: 1 Atomising, 5 Wan, 6 Gnu, 7 Margate, 10 Sol,
11 In irons, 12 Wee, 13 Obadiah, 16 Our, 17 Tar, 18 Incognito.
DOWN: 1 Angelica, 2 Ovum, 3 Swag, 4 Gamekeeper, 5 Welsh
Corgi, 8 Aorta, 9 Answer to, 14 Dodo, 15 Hopi.

161

ACROSS: 1 In safe hands, 5 Start up, 7 Trawl, 8 Halve, 9 Inlet,
11 Bison, 12 Wherein, 13 Record score. DOWN: 1 Into thin air,
2 Flail, 3 Hutch, 4 Siege engine, 5 Swallow, 6 Pulls in, 10 Their,
11 Bless.

162

ACROSS: 1 Air intakes, 5 Proposed, 9 Okra, 10 Frau,
11 Rumba, 12 Mess, 14 Toga, 15 Cribbage, 18 Bluebottle.
DOWN: 1 Autonomic, 2 In pairs, 3 Asp, 4 Sue, 6 Olympia, 7 Sir,
8 Drumtable, 10 Fattest, 13 Ski, 16 Rob, 17 Bye.

163

ACROSS: 1 Board rubber, 5 Prefabs, 9 Bloc, 10 Rely,
11 Often, 12 Olav, 13 Olio, 14 Granule, 16 Disoriented.
DOWN: 1 Blueblooded, 2 Amp, 3 Bus, 4 Ready for bed, 6 Recover,
7 Footmen, 8 Barn Owl, 14 Gas, 15 Eat.

164

ACROSS: 1 Go straight, 6 Join, 7 Lou, 8 Thou, 9 At school,
11 Potatoes, 14 Trap, 15 Den, 16 Ease, 17 Head gasket.
DOWN: 1 Gastropods, 2 Tijuana, 3 Ionic, 4 Hello, 5 Full report,
10 Hostess, 12 Tinge, 13 Trend.

165

ACROSS: 1 Legal eagles, 5 Was, 7 Moo, 8 Toronto, 10 Passage,
11 Left off, 14 Awe, 15 Fug, 16 Draughtsmen. DOWN: 1 Low
standard, 2 Lair, 3 Anon, 4 Stock margin, 6 Stipple, 7 Move off,
9 Onset, 12 Flag, 13 Omit.

166

ACROSS: 1 All but a few, 5 Crossbow, 9 Okra, 10 Soon, 11 Mambo,
12 Tops, 14 Near, 15 Card game, 18 Cottontail. DOWN: 1 Axiomatic,
2 Becalms, 3 Ass, 4 Woo, 6 Olympia, 7 Boo, 8 Wonderful,
10 Soonest, 13 Par, 16 Arc, 17 Get.

167

ACROSS: 1 Raise a cheer, 5 King Rat, 9 Yelp, 10 Ajar, 11 Re-run,
12 Ludo, 13 Iris, 14 Realist, 16 Rubber bands. DOWN: 1 Rugby
player, 2 Irk, 3 Eat, 4 Record sales, 6 Improve, 7 Gabriel,
8 Ananias, 14 Rub, 15 Tan.

168

ACROSS: 1 Go a long way, 7 Ovoid, 8 Irish, 9 Nagging pain, 11 Right
on time, 14 Laser, 15 Trope, 16 Goes too far. DOWN: 1 Ground
rule, 2 Among, 3 Old, 4 Going on, 5 Anita, 6 Change gear,
10 In turns, 12 Gismo, 13 In-off, 15 Two.

69

ACROSS: 1 Interaction, 5 Trieste, 8 Remit, 9 Bathe, 10 Copra, 12 Ovary, 14 Castled, 15 Not ring true. DOWN: 1 Instruction, 2 Totem, 3 Inept, 4 Nursery tale, 6 In-trays, 7 Subsoil, 11 Picot, 13 Adder.

170

ACROSS: 1 Admitting, 5 Eli, 6 Rut, 7 Tiny bit, 10 Ida, 11 Rhondda, 12 Zoe, 13 Ipswich, 16 Are, 17 Rid, 18 Lifeboats. DOWN: 1 Airfares, 2 Mutt, 3 Troy, 4 Goatsbeard, 5 Elliptical, 8 Ionic, 9 Braziers, 14 Wise, 15 Ha-ha.

171

ACROSS: 1 Bridle paths, 5 Noble, 7 Poser, 9 Ran away, 11 End, 12 Tit, 13 Exmouth, 16 Mushy, 17 Under, 18 Supper party. DOWN: 1 Bunjee jumps, 2 Lie-in, 3 Papaw, 4 Street party, 6 Borders, 8 Scythed, 10 Ago, 14 Maybe, 15 Usurp.

172

ACROSS: 1 Enchanting, 7 Light, 8 Webfoot, 11 Indri, 13 Testy, 14 Holds up, 16 Adorn, 18 Hop-picking. DOWN: 2 Nag, 3 Hotwires, 4 Toff, 5 Gratifying, 6 Flying high, 9 Brat pack, 10 Opus, 12 Deal, 15 Drop, 17 Own.

173

ACROSS: 1 Jack Hawkins, 5 Jonquil, 8 Bantu, 9 Evoke, 10 Ester, 12 Royal, 14 Pinched, 15 Razor shells. DOWN: 1 Jailbreaker, 2 Cajun, 3 Igloo, 4 Suede gloves, 6 Neutron, 7 Unearth, 11 Topaz, 13 Yodel.

174

ACROSS: 1 Absenting, 5 Cos, 6 Ski, 7 Passage, 10 Nor, 11 Trainee, 12 Coo, 13 Wide boy, 16 Ego, 17 The, 18 Excessive. DOWN: 1 Assorted, 2 Skip, 3 Tops, 4 Greenhouse, 5 Countywide, 8 Amigo, 9 Anecdote, 14 Ease, 15 Yeti.

175

ACROSS: 1 On your marks, 5 Shot off, 7 Toast, 8 Youth, 9 Owlet, 11 Cowls, 12 Display, 13 Ready-cooked. DOWN: 1 Open to offer, 2 U-boat, 3 Moody, 4 South Island, 5 Small ad, 6 Four-way, 10 Tasty, 11 Cello.

176

ACROSS: 1 About-turns, 5 Hose reel, 9 Mica, 10 Ploy, 11 Error, 12 Toad, 14 Peso, 15 Croziers, 18 Guinea pigs. DOWN: 1 Animistic, 2 U-shaped, 3 Use, 4 She, 6 Sunrise, 7 Eel, 8 Layabouts, 10 Props up, 13 Ago, 16 Rag, 17 Ion.

177

ACROSS: 1 Summit talks, 5 Would-be, 9 Airy, 10 Undo, 11 Masai, 12 Limp, 13 Seep, 14 Kaisers, 16 Retail trade. DOWN: 1 Suitable for, 2 Mow, 3 Lie, 4 School prize, 6 Olympia, 7 Lessons, 8 Bruiser, 14 Kit, 15 Spa.

178

ACROSS: 1 Fraternity, 6 Near, 7 Tea, 8 Luck, 9 Aviation, 11 Handbook, 14 Exit, 15 Mob, 16 Into, 17 Fair or foul. DOWN: 1 Feel at home, 2 Tankard, 3 Norma, 4 Tutti, 5 Dawn patrol, 10 Take-off, 12 Nubia, 13 Brier.

179

ACROSS: 1 Strong views, 5 Nap, 7 Boo, 8 Atlanta, 10 Abiding, 11 Eluding, 14 Eat, 15 Ere, 16 Straight bat. DOWN: 1 Sandhoppers, 2 Null, 3 Vein, 4 Scots accent, 6 Parapet, 7 Baggage, 9 Aided, 12 Ugli, 13 Inch.

180

ACROSS: 1 Almshouses, 5 Assent to, 9 Leaf, 10 Self, 11 Least, 12 Idol, 14 Plus, 15 Dark days, 18 Hypotenuse. DOWN: 1 Agile mind, 2 Scafell, 3 Use, 4 Set, 6 Samaria, 7 Tie, 8 Offensive, 10 Stops in, 13 Our, 16 Ash, 17 Duo.

81

CROSS: 1 Scaling down, 5 Sat back, 9 Norm, 10 Area, 11 Enter, 12 Bear, 13 Mind, 14 Day girl, 16 Short pastry. DOWN: 1 String bands, 2 Ass, 3 Oak, 4 Neat and tidy, 6 Almeria, 7 Batting, 8 Charmer, 14 Duo, 15 Lot.

182

ACROSS: 1 Fallen star, 7 Yucca, 8 Arise, 9 Radio aerial, 11 High fashion, 14 Drape, 15 Adapt, 16 Corked wine. DOWN: 1 Fly orchids, 2 Lucid, 3 Era, 4 Stamens, 5 Alibi, 6 Heel-and-toe, 10 Off-peak, 12 Guano, 13 Iraqi, 15 Aid.

183

ACROSS: 1 Love letters, 5 Scribes, 8 Enrol, 9 Queen, 10 Infra, 12 Idaho, 14 Non-skid, 15 Nailing down. DOWN: 1 Leif Ericson, 2 Visor, 3 Ensue, 4 Set in motion, 6 Relearn, 7 Be quick, 11 Fungi, 13 Audio.

184

ACROSS: 1 Producing, 5 Flu, 6 Tie, 7 Rhondda, 10 Lip, 11 Jam roll, 12 Ion, 13 Hubbies, 16 Ate, 17 Ran, 18 Priceless. DOWN: 1 Put-up job, 2 Over, 3 Cyan, 4 Gay abandon, 5 Feels cheap, 8 Horse, 9 Delivers, 14 Bloc, 15 Sage.

185

ACROSS: 1 Sweepstakes, 5 Audit, 7 Aorta, 9 Nailgun, 11 Ore, 12 Elm, 13 Drawing, 16 Ounce, 17 Badge, 18 Go to the dogs. DOWN: 1 Stay too long, 2 Petri, 3 Twang, 4 Scale models, 6 Dunedin, 8 Reneged, 10 Law, 14 Alert, 15 Imbue.

186

ACROSS: 1 Assailable, 7 Usurp, 8 Reawake, 11 Nacho, 13 Nadia, 14 Flashed, 16 Annul, 18 Lie in state. DOWN: 2 Sou, 3 Approach, 4 Anew, 5 Extendable, 6 Guinea fowl, 9 Abundant, 10 Aged, 12 Coda, 15 Sari, 17 Nit.

187

ACROSS: 1 Swallowed up, 5 Restful, 8 Polka, 9 Reeve, 10 Dates, 12 Accra, 14 Bravery, 15 Clown around. DOWN: 1 Slipped disc, 2 Aural, 3 Delve, 4 Pulled ahead, 6 Swansea, 7 Forsake, 11 Taboo, 13 Coypu.

188

ACROSS: 1 Abscising, 5 Her, 6 Rid, 7 Slivers, 10 Ran, 11 Grubs up!, 12 Its, 13 Ordeals, 16 Eli, 17 Nod, 18 Abhorring. DOWN: 1 Arranged, 2 Suds, 3 Spiv, 4 Goes to seed, 5 Henry Fonda, 8 Libel, 9 Expiring, 14 Echo, 15 Semi.

189

ACROSS: 1 Opinion poll, 5 In a mood, 7 Tribe, 8 Exult, 9 Afoot, 11 Igloo, 12 Stipend, 13 Right amount. DOWN: 1 Open trailer, 2 Inane, 3 No-one, 4 Light socket, 5 In irons, 6 Doubled, 10 Twist, 11 I-beam.

190

ACROSS: 1 Arthropods, 5 New World, 9 Epic, 10 Ha-ha, 11 Outdo, 12 Tamp, 14 Spiv, 15 Dogtooth, 18 Blumenthal. DOWN: 1 Alienated, 2 Hen coop, 3 Paw, 4 Sol, 6 Write to, 7 RNA, 8 Draw a veil, 10 Hotshot, 13 Mug, 16 Orb, 17 Ohm.

191

ACROSS: 1 Safari parks, 5 Naughty, 9 Lira, 10 Unto, 11 Harem, 12 Sale, 13 Plum, 14 Imitate, 16 Bell peppers. DOWN: 1 Singles club, 2 Fen, 3 Ray, 4 School meals, 6 Anaheim, 7 Gourmet, 8 Trumpet, 14 Ill, 15 Eye.

192

ACROSS: 1 Hockey team, 6 Name, 7 Dim, 8 Kiss, 9 Mansions, 11 Cut no ice, 14 Aloe, 15 Tip, 16 Coax, 17 Addressees. DOWN: 1 Hark back to, 2 Kinsman, 3 Teens, 4 Audio, 5 Amusements, 10 Ice axes, 12 Tepid, 13 Occur.

193

ACROSS: 1 Letting down, 5 Cat, 7 Was, 8 Samaria, 10 UEFA Cup, 11 Renewal, 14 Ave, 15 Mar, 16 Spanking new. DOWN: 1 Locust years, 2 Item, 3 Gear, 4 No score draw, 6 T-square, 7 Wax palm, 9 Apace, 12 Nook, 13 Wren.

194

ACROSS: 1 Auctioneer, 5 Pinholes, 9 UFOs, 10 Char, 11 Enrol, 12 Emir, 14 Agog, 15 Landseer, 18 Engine room. DOWN: 1 Augur well, 2 Tipster, 3 Nth, 4 Rue, 6 Neurone, 7 Lah, 8 Strong-arm, 10 Clearer, 13 Ion, 16 Ace, 17 Ski.

195

ACROSS: 1 Butterballs, 5 Omicron, 9 Idol, 10 Feed, 11 Atlas, 12 Zany, 13 Ever, 14 In trust, 16 Skyrocketed. DOWN: 1 Bat Mitzvahs, 2 Two, 3 LAN, 4 Stand around, 6 Malayan, 7 Collier, 8 Offsets, 14 Icy, 15 Tot.

196

ACROSS: 1 Fellowship, 7 Nerve, 8 Addle, 9 Learn a trade, 11 Offside rule, 14 Noise, 15 Ethyl, 16 Grey-haired. DOWN: 1 Final count, 2 Larva, 3 One, 4 Seattle, 5 India, 6 Bejewelled, 10 Naively, 12 Friar, 13 Usher, 15 Era.

197

ACROSS: 1 Pushing down, 5 Summits, 8 Nylon, 9 Caste, 10 Paper, 12 Their, 14 Walks on, 15 Rationality. DOWN: 1 Pen and paper, 2 Sisal, 3 Oasis, 4 New Year's Day, 6 Mineral, 7 Incites, 11 Pewit, 13 Ennui.

198

ACROSS: 1 Angelfish, 5 Hop, 6 Pro, 7 Wood ash, 10 DNA, 11 Lowlier, 12 Ova, 13 Grounds, 16 Aka, 17 Use, 18 For export. DOWN: 1 Appeal to, 2 Glow, 3 Find, 4 High praise, 5 Holding off, 8 Ogled, 9 Aeronaut, 14 Urge, 15 Sago.

199

ACROSS: 1 In detention, 5 Nurse, 7 Unfit, 9 Windsor, 11 Ems,
12 Eel, 13 Informs, 16 Maker, 17 Papua, 18 Near the mark.
DOWN: 1 Innocent man, 2 Tie in, 3 Nouns, 4 Not hold back,
6 Raw silk, 8 Fires up, 10 Duo, 14 First, 15 Rupee.

200

ACROSS: 1 Humanistic, 7 Rondo, 8 Mahouts, 11 Nadia, 13 Feign,
14 Crew cut, 16 Irate, 18 Engineered. DOWN: 2 Urn, 3 Aromatic,
4 Sago, 5 Cross-index, 6 Grand-scale, 9 Half-time, 10 Ugli,
12 Done, 15 Wadi, 17 Ape.

Build your puzzle collection with Hamlyn

Pitcherwits
Volume 1: 978-0-600-63421-8
Volume 2: 978-0-600-63490-4
Volume 3: 978-0-600-63491-1

Daily Mail All New Quick Crosswords
Volume 1: 978-0-600-62610-7
Volume 2: 978-0-600-62653-4
Volume 3: 978-0-600-62654-1
Volume 4: 978-0-600-62655-8
Volume 5: 978-0-600-62656-5
Volume 6: 978-0-600-62946-7
Volume 7: 978-0-600-62947-4
Volume 8: 978-0-600-63263-4
Volume 9: 978-0-600-63495-9

Daily Mail All New Cryptic Crosswords
Volume 1: 978-0-600-62609-1
Volume 2: 978-0-600-62657-2
Volume 3: 978-0-600-62658-9
Volume 4: 978-0-600-62659-6
Volume 5: 978-0-600-62652-7
Volume 6: 978-0-600-62948-1
Volume 7: 978-0-600-62949-8
Volume 8: 978-0-600-63270-2
Volume 9: 978-0-600-63496-6

Daily Mail Big Book of Cryptic Crosswords
Volume 1: 978-0-600-62169-0
Volume 2: 978-0-600-62215-4
Volume 3: 978-0-600-62470-7
Volume 4: 978-0-600-62620-6
Volume 5: 978-0-600-62951-1
Volume 6: 978-0-600-63264-1
Volume 7: 978-0-600-63494-2

Daily Mail Big Book of Quick Crosswords
Volume 1: 978-0-600-62170-6
Volume 2: 978-0-600-62216-1
Volume 3: 978-0-600-62469-1
Volume 4: 978-0-600-62621-3
Volume 5: 978-0-600-62950-4
Volume 6: 978-0-600-62952-8
Volume 7: 978-0-600-63265-8
Volume 8: 978-0-600-63493-5

Mail on Sunday Prize Crosswords
Volume 1: 978-0-600-62357-1
Volume 2: 978-0-600-62612-1

Mail on Sunday General Knowledge Crosswords
Volume 1: 978-0-600-63492-8

Mail on Sunday Super Sudoku
Volume 1: 978-0-600-62193-5
Volume 2: 978-0-600-62217-8
Volume 3: 978-0-600-62465-3
Volume 4: 978-0-600-62471-4
Volume 5: 978-0-600-62472-1
Volume 6: 978-0-600-62611-4
Volume 7: 978-0-600-63266-5

Daily Mail Big Puzzle Collection
978-0-600-62953-5

Daily Mail All New Giant Crosswords
978-0-600-63269-6

To buy the complete list of Daily Mail titles, visit
www.mailbookshop.co.uk